To my friends,
Zig & Martha

Anne Shepherd

# SARATOGA DIARY: 1912

by
**Anne D. Shepherd**

A Geneva Book

Carlton Press, Inc.          New York, N.Y.

This is Hortense's story,
But it is gratefully dedicated to the two people
Who helped most in its retelling:
To
DONALD
The baby with an illustrious future
and
In loving memory of
HAROLD
The spunky kid who grew up to be a Great Scout

# CONTENTS

# PROLOGUE

Every week for ten years I felt an agonizing depression if I went to Pinecrest and an unrelenting guilt if I didn't. Usually I went because of past love and loyalty, not because I suspected there was anything to gain. Aunt Hortense hadn't known anyone for years. Pitifully silent, she had shrunk into a helpless blob and simply waited for death.

"She must have been a real pretty lady when she was young. She has such beautiful skin and such beautiful eyes."

"I suppose so. I didn't know her then, but she was always neat and well-groomed."

"Was she married?"

"Yes, her husband died many years ago, but she told me once that she got married the year she was twenty."

The nurse's remark made me wonder: how had a twenty-year-old girl from St. Petersburg met a man, many years older than she, from Saratoga?

Children are too busy playing to listen to grown-up talk. Teenagers are too busy with their own loves to wonder about their relatives' love life. Young mothers are too busy raising their children to ask how their aunts and uncles met and courted.

I looked down at the mindless creature on the bed. Could this pathetic, stroke-damaged old body have ever had a life full of thrills and excitement? Could there be a story behind the brown eyes, if only her tongue were loosed so she could tell it? I had assumed that her life was drab, ordinary, and uneventful, but maybe I was wrong. Why had I always been too busy to ask my aunt to tell me about her life while she was able?

They say that when people approach death they can talk, even when they haven't done so for years.

"Oh, Auntie, talk to me! Can you hear me? Tell me about the times when you were young and beautiful and in love. Tell me about the year you got married. Tell me about your honeymoon. Was it exciting and glamorous? What romantic secrets are locked in your heart, Hortense? What would you tell me if you could talk?"

She had lost the ability to speak, but could her mind still find a sanctuary in reminiscences of a time long ago? Did she still dream of the adventures and passions of her youth? Did I bring her back from some enchanted place in the past, full of wonderful and delightful people each time I came?

"How did you meet your husband?" I wondered aloud, knowing she couldn't answer me.

People didn't travel as much back in those days, I mused. Why, they probably went on their honeymoon in a horse-drawn buggy! How in the world could they have met when they lived so far apart?

Hortense opened her mouth like a little bird each time I touched her lips with the spoon. When she had finished that unappetizing, strained dinner, I manicured her nails and checked the bed sore on her hip. It was deep and ugly, but it seemed to be healing around the edges this time.

I kissed her, waved good-bye to the wheelchair ladies gathered in the day room, and held my breath as I walked by the trash cans full of dirty chux in the hall.

Pinecrest was really no worse than the average nursing home, I supposed. On the outside the red brick building looked attractive. The wide grounds were shaded with magnolia, maple, mimosa, dogwood, redbud, and pine trees. The lawns were kept mowed and trimmed, and the flower beds near the entrance were bright with spring bulbs and summer annuals. Daffodils, pansies, and tulips were followed by geraniums, begonias, and then chrysanthemums. Red camellias and blue hydrangeas bloomed in their seasons next to the building. Hollies gave color to the winter with their berries.

Inside there were the smells—turnip greens and greasy pork, Lysol and wax, and the nauseating odor of the incontinent wing.

Then there were the screams and cries—

"I want my mama!"

"Oh, God, come and take me away from here!"

"Help me! Somebody help me!"

"My Jesus, I want to be with you."

"I want to go home!"

"Lord in Heaven, come down here and take me to live with you!"

In their apparently mindless raving, they were pitifully aware that the only escape from Pinecrest would have to be through death.

Why does God allow people to stay here this way? Most people would much rather be dead than to go on existing under these conditions.

Every week I chatted with Hortense's roommate, Mrs. Bell, but one day she only mumbled something unintelligible. She'd had a stroke. The next week her bed was empty. She had made good her escape from Pinecrest. I said a silent prayer for her. I would miss her and her friendly daughter, but I wouldn't grieve for her. She wouldn't suffer any more and was spared the vegetarian existence of my aunt. Numerous loving grandchildren and great-grandchildren survived her. What more could any woman ask for?

I pondered that question as I drove the twenty miles home, past the huge round stadium, the gleaming gold-domed capitol, the blue dome of the Regency, and the seventy-five-story Peachtree Plaza Hotel towering high above all the other buildings in Atlanta.

If only Hortense could have had children and grandchildren! Why had she never had children? If she wasn't able to have her own babies, she could have adopted some. I wondered why she hadn't done that.

I kept hoping for a miracle so she could talk to me before she died and tell me about the happy and sad memories tucked away in her mind, but it never came.

At last Hortense made the trip to "The Grady" in the red and white ambulance for the last time. Her breathing was labored. Her brown eyes held a frightened look. There were tubes leading to and from her body. I patted her hand and washed her feverish face with a damp cloth. The doctor said he didn't have much hope that she would live through the night, and she didn't. She was eighty-five years old. For many years she had wanted only to join her beloved husband in Heaven. Now her wish had finally been granted. Death was a blessed release.

She had died without revealing any of the romantic secrets of her youth. I had never really believed that she would rouse up and answer all my questions, but still I felt a tremendous sense of disappointment.

Her money had been used up in the long years of nursing home care. The legacy she left her heirs consisted of four boxes of mementoes that were put away after her first stroke. My brother and I opened the boxes and examined our treasures.

One held old canceled checks. We threw it in the trash. Two held old-fashioned doilies and dresser scarves, once-lovely hand-embroidered towels, sheets, aprons, and pillowcases, now stained and useless.

In the last box we found a souvenir folder from Atlanta, several picture postcards from a small town called Hastings, Florida in horse-and-buggy days, and several from Lake George, New York. Next I pulled out some photographs I had never seen before. One was a charming picture of a bearded old man sitting in a wagon loaded with baskets of grapes, with a pair of horses waiting to pull the wagon to market. The next picture must have been my uncle as a young man, looking very debonair in a top coat, gloves, and hat. A lovely photograph of a poised young lady wearing a dark suit, gloves, and a hat with a huge, curving ostrich plume quite took my breath away. The big, soul-searching brown eyes told her identity. It had to be the young Hortense!

Near the bottom of the box was a small package wrapped carefully and neatly in several thicknesses of tissue. It was labeled "Rocks from Mount McGregor." Inside were three smooth stones about the size and shape of goose eggs. I loved the way they felt in my hands.

The last thing in the box was a small, nondescript-looking book marked "Datebook 1912." It didn't look like anything special on the outside—not important at all. I picked it up. It fitted comfortably on the palm of my hand. And from that moment my life was changed.

I opened the book and Charlotte Bush's spidery, old-fashioned handwriting seemed to reach out and capture me. Here was a treasury of nostalgia from a bygone era pictured so vividly that I was transported instantly to a very special time and place. The characters in the diary surrounded me and clamored for me to relive the year with them, promising to answer all my questions about the romance of the young Hortense. They would also reveal a strange and unexpected drama in the "uneventful" life of Hortense Bush.

# A NEW YEAR
## Chapter 1

At bedtime Lottie Bush always recorded the day's events in her diary and then spent a long time sorting out her thoughts. Tonight, as usual, she was especially troubled about Stanley, although she didn't write about that. Every page would be filled with her worries over Stanley, if she put them all down.

What was really going on down there in Florida? Why couldn't he tell her about what had happened between him and Lulu? Didn't he understand that his mother wanted to be needed—to comfort him in his troubles and advise him with his problems? What had been the last straw that made him leave his wife and take a job a thousand miles away from her?

Lottie wrote to him regularly, asking questions like: "Are you happy? Have you heard from Lulu? Are you going to try to make up with her? Do you think you'll ever move back to Saratoga?"

Stanley wrote back cheerfully every week or two saying, "It's warm here—shirt sleeve weather! Tomatoes and cucumbers ripe—strawberries too! How much snow do you have there?"

Lottie sighed. Stanley wouldn't take advice from anybody, anyway. She had warned him four years ago not to marry Lulu. What would this new year of 1912 bring for poor, ill-starred Stanley, she wondered. Would it bring him any measure of happiness, or would it only bring more distress? Would it bring tranquility or turmoil? Every mother worries more about one child than the others, and Stanley was Lottie's particular concern.

She dipped her pen in the inkwell and wrote, "At eleven twenty-three tonight George will have been dead one year. . . ."

How lonesome the year had been without him! He had hated being an invalid though, and Ray had managed the farm just as well as his father ever did, thank the Lord. But what she missed most was their conversations. She and Ray talked a lot but only

11

on a practical, superficial level. Somehow mother and son could not express their thoughts on a deeper level. Unspoken thoughts thus often grew into torturous forebodings.

Shaking off her gloom, the old woman smiled at the memory of how quaint Harold had been this morning, talking between bites of buckwheat cakes, maple syrup dripping down his chin.

"Have a Happy New Year, Gramma. You have one too, Pa, and you, Ma, and you too, Uncle Ray!"

The eager little boy had beamed at each one in turn as if he were handing out presents.

Then he said excitedly, "I know it'll be a good year f'r me, 'cause I'll start t' school in September, right after Labor Day. That's what Ma says."

Lottie hoped the other children would accept Harold. He was a very friendly child—but would they tease him about his disability? He was so spunky and independent she supposed she really didn't need to worry. Even on the steep back stairway he wouldn't let anyone help him, but insisted on dragging himself up or down with his slow whish, bump—whish, bump.

Poor Harold. She was afraid he would never be any better. It was a shame that he would never march to the music of his favorite song. He would always have to crawl or scoot himself along the floor in his funny way. The only consolation was that he hadn't died when he was so ill a year and a half ago.

Lottie blew out the candle and snuggled down under the heavy quilts and blankets. It would be nice to have Mary and Harold here all week—too bad Clifford couldn't stay too, but they were taking inventory at the store today and he would have to work all week.

She closed her eyes and reflected drowsily what a nice day it had been. They had all enjoyed the music from Clif's new gramophone. What a wonderful invention! All her friends must come over this week so they could hear it.

She fell asleep and dreamed that the state was paving the road. That was the only explanation she could think of for the nine wagon loads of dirt that had gone by today. She'd heard that it would be one of the first roads in the state to be paved, since it was the main highway from New York to Montreal.

Next morning she baked a "choc'lit" cake for Harold and sent invitations to all the neighbors to visit while Mary and Harold

12

were here. Then they took the gramophone and piled in the buggy to visit their nearest neighbors, the Myers. Grace would love the music.

Sure enough, Grace was thrilled when "Let Me Call You Sweetheart" came floating out like magic from the big, flaring speaker.

"Wouldn't it be wonderful to have a gramophone of our own, Mother Myers?" she exclaimed.

"With the baby coming, I don't think John will be able to buy you one any time soon, Grace."

Lottie spoke up. "I'm going to have one as soon as Clif can order it for me. Ray and I sit alone reading night after night, and we could have music while we read. I'll miss it when Clif takes it back home next weekend. I know it's extravagant, but I've saved up $25 from my butter and eggs."

"Ma, put on 'Alexander's Ragtime Band' for Miss Grace! That's my fav'rite song," Harold shrilled. He used the floor as his drum to beat time to the music.

"Come on 'n hear . . ." he sang off key, as he thumped the floor.

While the women chatted and listened to music, Harold looked at picture books, and Ray went to do his errands. Later he came back with the mail and said that Pratt had agreed to pay $28 for the fat cow. That further justified Lottie's determination to buy a graphophone. She felt quite wealthy.

She didn't feel so good about the news in Stanley's letter when she read it on the way home.

"Stanley says he's met a lady in the general store at Hastings. Her name is Hortense Estes, and she's beautiful and charming."

Ray grunted, "What a dumb name! She's probably also a good dancer, stupid, and can't cook, sew, or clean."

His face was dark and sullen as he spoke. The intensity of his malice toward his brother surprised Lottie. She had hoped they had outgrown that fierce hatred.

"Now, Ray, that was unkind! Stanley made a mistake once, but he's older now. I'm sure he has better judgement now."

Lottie wasn't convinced that Stanley's judgement had improved, but she had to defend him against Ray's bitter attack. It was odd when Ray was such a kind and gentle man around other people—and animals too. Privately she was inclined to agree with his diatribe, but she didn't want Ray to know that.

I wonder if he's dating this Hortense person, and him a married

13

man! Young folks these days don't seem to take their marriage vows as seriously as George and I did forty years ago, she thought.

Even though Stanley had been separated from his wife nearly a year, she believed that it was morally wrong for him to have a new sweetheart. She knew he was impulsive and impetuous, but with his new job in Florida he seemed to be settling down into a steady worker. Was that only wishful thinking? Was he really still the same brash, foolish young man about to make another mistake?

When the news that he had started his divorce action came two weeks later, she feared the worst. She knew she should trust Stanley to straighten out his life. But what would all her friends say about a divorce in her family? It was quite scandalous. She felt embarrassed and humiliated. It was a disgrace. She didn't know if she could face her friends. For the next two weeks she brooded silently about his imprudence.

Stanley had requested that Lottie send him his dress coat, two low cut vests, and his dress shirt. There was to be a Leap Year Dance at Palatka on January 19. Dutifully Lottie packed up his dress suit and mailed it—the postal charge was eighty-six cents.

"There, Ma," said Ray spitefully. "Didn't I tell you Hortense would be a dancing girl? I'll bet she doesn't know how to do anything but dress up fancy and go dancing. Stanley gets himself up in his best clothes and makes the girls think he's rich. All they want to do is go out socializing and dancing all the time."

Ray was sure he would never feel anything but hate and scorn for any woman who liked Stanley. He cocked his head on one side, put a smirk on his face, bowed with mock ceremony, and said primly, "May I have the honor of this dance, Miss Estes?" with his large frame in such a mincing pose he looked ridiculous.

"Stop that, Ray! Don't mimic Stanley that way. He's worked hard this year down there at the Nix Company. He deserves to have some fun occasionally. Besides you don't know anything about this woman, Hortense. She may be a very nice lady. She works at the general store, he said, so she's not just a flirt and a dancer."

But secretly Lottie began to worry about what sort of person Hortense was. She was suspicious of her motives in dating Stanley. Maybe Ray was right and she did think he was rich. Stanley must be serious about her or he wouldn't have started the divorce

14

proceedings. How soon would she get to meet her, she wondered. Somehow she was sure she wouldn't like Hortense any better than she had liked Lulu.

# COMMON GOSSIP
## Chapter 2

Throughout the bitter cold days of winter, Lottie kept busy indoors and seldom ventured out in the snow. She had plenty of time to think and philosophize while she worked, and it was not a bad life. On the whole she was really quite happy.

Ray was content with his life on the farm also. Every day of the year he was busy doing strenuous work outdoors in all kinds of weather, but he loved most of it.

It was only the butchering that he hated. He loved the animals too much to want to kill them for food, but he had to be practical—he knew that. On January 17th when the temperature dropped very low and snow covered the ground, Ray got his friend, Clarence Whealey, to help him butcher the young bull and the big hog. Ray's knife was sharp and swift, and the bull opened his mouth to bellow, but instead slumped quietly to the ground. Ray turned away so Clarence wouldn't tease him about his tears, because of the imploring look in the big, liquid eyes of the friend he had cared for since his birth last year. Soon the bull's life was dripping down from the scaffold into puddles on the snow. The hog let out one long, awful squeal before the knife silenced him. When the animals were finally still, Ray could get at the hard day's work without any further qualms.

They dipped the pig into the scalding kettle and then began scraping off its hair. All day while they worked, the men gossiped. Ray had to answer a lot of questions about Stanley's divorce and his new lady friend, but mainly they talked about the fire on the mountain the night before. Clarence had heard all the details down at the general store early that morning.

"Could you see the flames from your place, Ray?"

"Sure could. What was it—do you know?"

"It was one of those temporary residence buildings for the workmen building the sanitarium," he informed Ray.

"Ma was afraid it was Grant Cottage, but I knew it wasn't the right place. What caused it? Do you have any idea?"

"One of those Italian workers lit a candle and walked around—caught the bedclothes on fire. 'Stead-a putting out the fire while it was small, he ran from one end to the other yelling f'r everybody to get out! They all got out, but the building was burned to the ground!"

Ray shook his head sadly. "Guess that'll slow the Metropolitan down on building the sanitarium. They'll have to build another residence hall now."

"Say, you know, I've heard the sanitarium will have over 300 patients when it's finished!"

"That so? Lotta folks around here opposed to having a sanitarium so close to Wilton. You reckon anybody'd catch tuberculosis with them up there on Mount McGregor?"

"Naw. I don't think so. Whole place is gonna be real scientific. They say it's a real good climate to cure tuberculosis."

As each of the neighbors passed by the Bush farm that day he had to comment on the fire as well as check up on the butchering operation. Dallas Varney bought a forward quarter of the beef for $6, and John Richards paid $6.51 for a hind quarter. Clarence would receive some of the pork as his pay.

Ray had many friends throughout the county and he got along well with everybody. He delighted in discussing politics or the events of the day with men down at the general store or post office. Children were special to Ray too—of course, his nephew, Harold, was his favorite. He could talk to children and charm them with stories about animals or life on the farm. Old ladies were enchanted by his gentlemanly attention, but when a young lady was present he was tongue-tied.

Ray was essentially a happy man. The only thing he would change about his life would be to have a wife. She wouldn't have to be beautiful. Clif's wife, Mary, wasn't beautiful. He only wanted someone to love, a woman to share his bed and give him a son—and perhaps a daughter too.

If only he could talk to a marriageable young lady! For some reason he was awkward and stupid when he met a girl. Nothing he said ever came out the way he meant it. He had tried many

17

times, but all the girls he knew had married someone else. That's why he began imagining a woman to keep him company.

Ray's fantasizing never hurt anyone; in fact nobody knew about it except for the farm animals, and they never told. Most of his work was solitary, of necessity, and the long chats with his imaginary lover warded off a lot of boredom through the long hours of toil. Not that he didn't enjoy his work, but he felt a very strong emotional as well as physical need for a partner to whom he could communicate all his inmost thoughts and desires. He dutifully reported to Ma everything he did, but many thoughts were too intimate for her ears. He would have been horribly embarrassed if she had overheard some of the sensuous remarks that Alban and Delmar heard routinely.

After thinking of her as "wife" for many months, Ray had begun to call her "Eve." She encouraged him in every achievement, soothed him in every failure, persuaded him always to work for self-improvement in every way. She was soft and pliant, strong and enduring, warm and loving, supportive and helpful. She was his ideal, his model, his image of perfection. For each chore done well, "Eve" was lavish in her praise.

"How straight and even your rows are!"

"How neatly you tied the grapevines, dearest."

"What a beautiful vegetable garden!"

"You must be very proud of that, darling."

"Congratulations on doing such a good job."

Everywhere he went she was there, but when others were present she hid behind him. Advice she would give willingly and constructively, but criticism, never. Her comfort and love were always available when he was sad or discouraged, but she never pushed herself on him unbidden. Like a good servant, she was always ready when he called for her.

In Ray's mind he had imbued her with all the best human qualities, but he had neglected to ascribe to her any faults or imperfections. There was no possibility that he would ever find a real person that would fill all his requirements, but still he searched each new girl's face and hoped that this one would turn out to be his "Eve." Here he was, thirty-six years old and still not married.

And yet that simpleton, Stanley, had apparently found two women willing to marry him! That was another thing he would

18

change about his life, if he could, Ray admitted. He wished his brother, Stanley, had never been born. Ma was always talking about him—Stanley needs his dress suit; Stanley says there's going to be a dance; Stanley is doing so well at the potato company; Stanley is in love with a beautiful lady. Damn Stanley! Ray could get along with everybody in the world except Stanley. He hoped his brother never came home again. It was better not to think about him.

January was a busy month and Ray had much to do while the cold weather held. He cut up part of the beef into roasts and steaks. He helped Ma make brine for the hams, mixing the salt, brown sugar, saltpeter and molasses in a big tub of boiling water, and poured it onto the hams and bacon in the barrels after it was cool.

John Myers was cutting the ice on Sprott's Pond into huge cakes, each weighing at least two hundred pounds, with his ice saw, chisel, and fork. Then Ray took the pike pole and floated the cakes to the platform, where he could ease them up a ramp with the tongs and push them onto his ice rack on the double sleighs.

In all Ray harvested 137 cakes of the pure bluish ice, filling the ice house, and tamping it with snow. Then he brought a wagon-load of sawdust from the mill to pack around the ice. He paid John Myers $2.74 for cutting the ice—two cents a cake.

After stamping his feet on the porch to shake off the snow, Ray burst in the kitchen and reported, "It's twenty-four degrees below zero down at the pond, Ma."

"I'm not surprised. I just read in the *Saratogian* that several barges were frozen in on the Hudson River." Then she added wistfully, "I wish we could have gone to the performance of the "Messiah" last night at Skidmore School of the Arts. The paper says 1500 people went."

"It's just too cold in January for that long trip at night, Ma. Say, that mincemeat pie smells wonderful! Cut me a piece now, will you? I can't wait 'til supper!"

She put a fourth of a pie on a plate for him. While he ate, he leafed through his *Sheep Breeder* magazine, always interested in the latest farming methods like a true agriculturist.

"Ma, do you think there's any truth to Stanley's claim that he's eating tomatoes and strawberries in January? We'll be lucky to get our tomato plants in the ground by the middle of June!"

19

"Stanley's not a liar, son. If he says he is, then he is. It does seem amazing, doesn't it?"

Ray shook his head. "Not amazing—impossible!"

Lottie started some pork chops sizzling in the iron skillet.

"How's the new calf, Ray? It's been too cold for me to go out to the barn to see her."

"Fine, Ma. Would you like me to walk her over so's you can see her? No need in you getting out in all that snow."

"I'd dearly love to see the little creature, Ray, but don't get her chilled on my account."

"She won't be out more'n a minute or two—'twon't hurt her. I'll lead her to where you can see out the window."

Watching out the parlor window Lottie saw just the little ears sticking up over the snow beside Ray's path to the barn. The snow was higher than the tiny calf's head. She stepped out on the piazza to see better.

"What a dear little thing she is! Let's name her 'Nutmeg'."

One morning when a snowstorm had just passed, the sun came out and shone on the new snow with dazzling brilliance. Lottie put on her furs and got Ray to drive her to visit Aunt Lydia Staples in the cutter. He tucked the buffalo robe around her and put two hot bricks wrapped in flannel under her feet, so she was toasty warm.

The fields stretched out for a quarter of a mile with their cool white blanket undisturbed between the road and the mountain. Mount McGregor made a white silhouette against the blue sky, with some dark spots, where the hemlocks and pines were just able to peep out with a touch of green from beneath their burden of snow. In the morning quiet the song of the sleigh bells seemed to echo off the mountain. The Bush's sleigh made the first tracks on the road toward Wilton.

Lottie breathed deeply of the crisp, fresh air and tried to decide which season she liked best. Riding like this in the cutter was certainly her favorite part of winter. Ray urged Alban to go faster. Gliding across the snow like this was so exhilarating—why, they must be going ten or fifteen miles an hour!

Since Lottie first heard the rumor that Aunt Lydia was going to sell her entire farm of 183 acres to the Metropolitan for the use of the sanatorium, she had been on fire with curiosity. She couldn't wait to see Aunt Lydia and hear all about it.

While Ray did his errands, Lydia Staples was happy to provide Lottie with all the latest details on the improvements the Metropolitan planned to make.

". . . and they're going to run electricity to all the buildings," she said importantly. "They're dickering for four other farms nearby, so they'll have at least 500 acres."

"Really? I wonder who else will sell to them—they approached me about buying my farm, but I wouldn't sell to them."

"I don't know, but Will Green's going to be Head Farmer."

Lottie nodded vigorously in approval. "I'm sure he'll be an excellent man for the job."

Aunt Lydia leaned forward and gazed straight into Lottie's eyes as she changed the subject abruptly and asked a searching question. "Is Stanley getting a divorce?"

Lottie had avoided her friends for the last two weeks, dreading that question. She was mortified. She crumpled her handkerchief and then smoothed it out again before she answered.

"Yes, I'm sorry to say he is."

"Well, don't be so upset about that, Lottie. 'Tisn't your fault, you know," Lydia said tartly.

Everyone respected Aunt Lydia's opinions. She was the matriarch of the whole village. Her comment made Lottie feel better immediately.

"Stanley and Lulu have been separated for almost a year now, but I hate to see a divorce in the family. I feel ashamed and embarrassed."

"Why not get a divorce if they can't live together? Never did think those two were suited for each other. No need for you to be ashamed of that. Does Stanley have a new lady friend?"

"All I know is he took a woman named Hortense Estes to the Leap Year Dance in Palatka. Sent for his dress suit. It must have been a fancy shindig. I just hope he isn't going to make another mistake."

"Don't try to live his life for him, my dear. He has to make his own mistakes and live with the consequences."

Lottie sighed. "I know you're right Aunt Lydia, but I do hope he will marry someone who is settled and mature next time; not someone else who is only interested in parties and dancing." After a moment she added wistfully, "It would be awful nice to have another grandchild or two—especially a little girl."

It was a relief when Lottie found that her other friends in and around the village agreed with Aunt Lydia. They didn't hold Stanley's divorce against her. It became common gossip for the next few weeks, but no one pointed a finger at his mother for not raising him right or not advising him properly. Lottie began to hold up her head again and visit with her friends from time to time as the weather allowed. She and Ray went on with their winter tasks without saying too much about Stanley, which suited Ray just fine. He hoped Stanley would go ahead and marry that trollop and settle down to live in Florida for the rest of his life. If he never saw Stanley again that would suit Ray just fine.

# APPLECAKE AND CINNAMON
## Chapter 3

On Candlemas Day Ray started drawing logs down from the side of the mountain on the heavy sleighs. Alban and Delmar pulled three loads the first day and kept going back for about a week, bringing the trees he had cut down last summer and left to season. Some of the big, straight ones would make fine boards. Ray would take them to Johnson's mill later. The others would be firewood for the kitchen stove.

While Ray worked outside, Lottie made doughnuts, mince pies, and their favorite applecake. As the aroma of the spicy applecake wafted through the house, she thought back to last spring when the apple trees were in bloom and she had sketched the lambs frisking under the pale pink blossoms. Now was a good time to paint that canvas, while it was too cold for any yard work. She got most of the background in, but ran out of blue for the sky.

"I'll get you some more when I go to Saratoga, Ma."

It was very cold the following Saturday when Ray rode the trolley to Saratoga, nine miles away. There wasn't anyone he knew on the car, and he sat alone, thinking how nice it would be to have a real "Eve" as a lifetime companion—someone soft and feminine, cheerful and talkative. He wouldn't be fussy about her appearance, but it would be nice if she was a good cook like Ma. Life is pretty hard on a big farm like ours, he admitted. It would be nice if his dream wife could be a hard worker too. Of course, as long as Ma lived, his wife wouldn't have to do much besides love him and bear his children. Then when Ma was gone, "Eve" could take over the churning, cooking, canning, and cleaning.

In Saratoga he talked to Van Deusen at the store on Broadway about buying his extra hay, made a few calls, bought Lottie's oil paint, and brought back the awful news that everybody had been talking about everywhere he went!

"Ma!" he called excitedly, as he slammed the door, "the Gansevoort Post Office burned down last night! They say the whole community was threatened by fire!"

"Mercy! How did it happen?"

"It was in the middle of the night—the Post Office and the house next door burned at a loss of between $200 and $250! It was terrible! When the train came through town, the engineer saw the fire and kept tooting his whistle 'til everybody got up!"

Ray was quite out of breath from this rapid recitation.

"Was anyone hurt?"

"No. The house was vacant. They think the fire might have started from the stove in the Post Office."

"Was all the mail lost?"

"No. Luckily Postmaster Carpenter always takes the mail and stamps home with him at night f'r safekeeping. He had $3 or $4 worth of stamps too, so it's a good thing he saved 'em!"

"That's a relief! I'm truly frightened of fire. Even with such a fine volunteer fire department, we seem so helpless if anything starts to burn. Ever since I watched the Hotel Balmoral burn, I've been afraid. What a terrible feeling it must be to watch your own home devoured by flames!"

Ray nodded in agreement, as he handed her the tube of Van Antwerp blue, a new artist brush, the mail, and two magazines.

"You got two March *Cosmopolitans*. I don't think you're ever going to get your subscription straightened out, Ma." Ray grinned as he spoke.

"My lands! I'll have to write to them again. I wish they'd send my January issue—I never got it."

She glanced at the mail and said dejectedly, "No letter from Stanley yet," but she perked up when she saw a letter from Mary.

Mary's letter saying that she and Clif had taken Harold to Albany to be fitted for a brace was almost as exciting as the post office fire. Clif had also sent a list of graphophone models for her to choose from.

Lottie began to hum "Let me call you sweetheart . . ." as she perused the catalog. She could hardly wait to have her own machine! Finally she decided on the Victor-Victrola Talking Machine VI, which was $25 in oak—"His Master's Voice," they called it.

After making that big decision, she started again on her apple piece. As she painted, she thought about Harold and was glad that Clif and Mary had decided to put a brace on him. He would have trouble when he started school, if he couldn't walk upright like other children. Maybe this would strengthen his legs, and later he wouldn't need the brace. What a dear child! And what funny little grown-up speeches he made! Of course he was accustomed to being around grown-ups more than children, so he mimicked adult conversation.

Now Lottie was ready to put in the gnarled old trees with their blush of spring blossom. She wanted it to look so real that the viewer would almost smell the delicate fragrance of the blooms and feel the soft breeze of a spring day. Last May she had been too busy with the spring cleaning and planting to have time to paint. After a quick sketch, she had promised herself to finish it in the winter when she was not so busy.

Now as she worked on it, the memory was strong and clear—the lambs leaping and running, the older sheep lying peacefully in the sunshine, each apple tree resembling a pale pink puff with tiny new green leaves just starting to emerge. The grass was a fresh spring green, and meadow flowers had sprung up under the trees. There was a serenity in the scene that gave peace to the soul.

Lottie was happy when she was painting. The usual persistent worry about Stanley had tried to invade her thoughts, but she had pushed it away and devoted herself completely to her work. She knew that a worrier doesn't produce a good artwork.

When the winter sun began to go down behind the mountain, she cleaned her brushes reluctantly. By the lamplight after supper she would embroider for a while. Maybe Clif and Mary could use a new chamber towel, she thought, or maybe she would save it for Stanley. If he was going to marry that woman, she would need a wedding present for them. Now what was her name? Oh, yes, Hortense. What an awful name. Probably an awful woman too.

The weather was unpredictable—sometimes so cold that Lottie moved her blankets and quilts down to the parlor to sleep on the couch near the coal stove, but then two or three sunshiny days made the snow look quite honey-combed. When some of the snow melted, Ray dug a big clump of parsnips and set the whole clod of frozen soil in a tub inside to thaw. It would be nice to have some delicious parsnips for dinner. For a few days it even got warm enough to let the fires go out, giving Lottie a chance to blacken and polish both stoves.

Early one Sunday morning in late February, Ray was distressed to find that one of their pigs had died—evidently having choked on something it ate. It made him very sad to think of the poor animal's agony. Then too it meant a financial loss of several dollars for him and his mother.

When Clif's wagon turned into the yard after breakfast, Ray and Lottie were instantly cheered by Harold's shout, "Gramma, Uncle Ray, we brought you some candy!"

Lottie gave Harold a big hug when Clif lifted him to the porch.

"Why, you have your brace now, Harold!"

"Yes, an' I c'n walk by myself now, Gramma. Aren't you s'prised?"

"That's wonderful, dear!" she exclaimed, giving him an extra hug. "We have a surprise for you too."

"What is it?" Harold's eyes were bright with anticipation.

Ray put his arm around Harold affectionately and said, "You come with me to the barn, and I'll show you the surprise."

He helped the eager little boy across the patches of snow to the big L-shaped barn, past the stables, and down to the sheep barn. There "Cinnamon" was standing proudly by her twin ewe lambs born just last Wednesday—the first lambs born on the farm this year. They were cavorting around, jumping on some boards and chasing each other back and forth, acting like silly little children playing first Leap Frog and then Follow the Leader. Harold laughed until his sides ached. Suddenly he remembered.

"Watch me walk, Uncle Ray! I'll catch them!"

He strutted slowly and carefully toward them. They teased him by running away just as he got near them. One climbed up on some boxes in a corner of the barn and then jumped like a daring trapeze artist. Harold stood there laughing at her crazy antics, and abruptly the other twin came up beside him. Harold grasped the soft fleece in his little fist, then stroked the tiny head before the playful imp was gone again, chasing after her sister.

"What're their names, Uncle Ray?"

"We haven't named them yet, Harold. You c'n name them, if you like."

"Oh, goody. C'n I name this one Curly and that one Jumpy?"

"Sure, fella. Those'd be fine names."

Ray felt sick inside at the sight of his young nephew struggling so hard to take a few steps with that bulky, cumbersome brace. He didn't know what to say when Harold asked earnestly, "Don't you think I c'n walk good, Uncle Ray?"

Finally he answered by saying, "Let's go show Grandma how you c'n walk, Harold. I think you're doing just fine."

The house smelled delicious when they got inside.

"What smells so good, Gramma? What's for dinner?"

"That's the sparerib from the hog Uncle Ray butchered last month—the last of the fresh pork," she added aside to Clif and Mary.

"Oh, boy! Watch me walk, Gramma!" Harold demanded.

He walked stiffly back and forth. His steps were awkward and slow. He wouldn't win any races, but he was walking upright, no hands on the floor. He came laboriously back to Lottie, waiting for her approval.

"I think you're doing wonderfully, Harold!" she said, clapping her hands. "And I know you'll get better and better as you get more used to the brace. Come in the kitchen with me. I have something for you."

She held his hand, and they walked back to the kitchen together. She reached in her sugar bowl and pulled out a dollar.

"Here's a dollar for you to spend any way you want to. I'm so proud of you, Harold!"

"Wow! Thank you, Gramma. I'll get Pa to take me with him t' the store tomorrow t' pick out something."

He was plodding back toward the parlor to show his mother what Gramma had given him when he stopped abruptly and shouted, "Gramma, where'd you get this pi'ture of the apple orchard?"

She came running at his shout, thinking he had fallen. He was standing close to the painting, sniffing at the apple trees. He wrinkled his nose, when he smelled the oil paint.

"I'm painting that, Harold. It isn't quite finished yet. Do you like it?"

"Oh, yes, indeed I do! Is it f'r me?" he piped enthusiastically.

"Why, no, dear. I plan to put that in the parlor. I really need a picture in there. Would you like me to paint you a picture?"

"I'd love t' have one in my room. I really need a pi'ture in there. Will you paint one f'r me, when you finish yours?"

27

"Of course I will, dear. What would you like me to paint for you?"

He thought a moment with his eyes shut tight, remembering last summer on the farm.

"I think I'd like a clover pi'ture," he said slowly. "You 'member when I picked a punch of clover f'r you, and you put it in your green bowl on the dining room table? You think you could paint that, Gramma?"

"I'm sure I can, Harold. And very soon too. Maybe the next time you come to see me I'll have it finished."

She smiled at his dear, funny repetition of her grown-up language, "I really need a pi'ture in there."

When Clif had a chance to take Ray aside for a moment, he questioned him about Stanley's plans.

"I don't know, Clif," he answered in surprise. "There's no figuring what Stanley will do. I suppose he'll just stay on in Florida. Maybe he's going to marry the woman he met down there. In any case I don't think he'll be coming home."

Clif pursed his lips and shook his head. "I'm not so sure about that. I have a notion he might bring the lady here to meet Ma."

"Why would he do that? He certainly doesn't think he has to have Ma's approval to marry her."

"I know, but I have a feeling he'll come here on his honeymoon, if he gets married again."

Oh, God! Ray had been so happy thinking that Stanley was going to stay in Florida. Now he had that to worry about. He wished Clif hadn't mentioned it.

John Myers was carrying a gun when he stopped by on his way up the mountain one day. He was trying to track down the fox that had been barking and prowling around all the chickens in the neighborhood.

"Here's a pamphlet on infantile paralysis, Lottie. I thought you'd be interested."

"Indeed I am! Thank you, John. How's Grace feeling?"

"She's mighty tired of waiting for the baby, Lottie—very uncomfortable and isn't sleeping well. It won't be long now, I'm sure, but meanwhile she's miserable."

"I've had a bad cold and bronchial trouble myself. I'm sorry I haven't been able to get out to see Grace."

28

"Don't you worry about Grace. Ma's taking good care of her. You stay in and keep warm."

"Thank you kindly for the pamphlet, John. I'll read it and pass it on to Mary. I hope you get that fox!"

Lottie sat down and read straight through the Public Health Bulletin about Poliomyelitis, hoping for some shred of comforting news—some possibility of treatment or therapy that would help Harold to regain the full use of his wasted legs.

Translating the technical language carefully, she decided that Harold's paralysis was permanent. It had been a year and a half since his illness. He would never be any better. The pamphlet had urged the prevention of deformities by the use of mechanical appliances. They mean like the brace Clif and Mary got for Harold, she decided.

Maybe some day someone would find a cure for this terrible disease. There would be no cure for Harold as long as he lived. If they were lucky, he would learn to walk well enough with the brace that his affliction would not be very noticeable. Harold had crawled like a baby—no, more like a monkey, she thought—for over a year. He looked so much better standing up where he could look everyone in the eye.

Lottie was getting anxious about Stanley. Usually he tried to write once a week, but she hadn't heard from him in over two weeks. Could anything be wrong? Even when he did write his letters were always choppy and uninformative, so she had written asking him to describe Hastings and what life was like there.

The unwritten questions she yearned to ask were: "Are you still seeing Hortense? What does she look like? What sort of person is she? What are you planning to do when your divorce becomes final later this month?"

She hoped she would get a letter soon. A day or two later her wish was granted. When Ray came back from Wilton he brought a fat letter from Stanley. It was so heavy it had taken three two-cent stamps to mail it. Lottie ripped it open eagerly and found nine picture postcards showing Hastings from several angles.

Spreading them out on the kitchen table, she examined the pictures avidly. She wondered if the building on down Hastings Boulevard from the hotel wasn't the store where Hortense worked. Stanley hadn't mentioned her in his last letter, so maybe the

29

romance was over. Lottie dipped her pen in the inkwell and began writing a long letter to Stanley.

The Gables
Wilton, New York
March 10, 1912

*My Dear Son,*

*I can't tell you how much we appreciate the nine post-cards from Hastings. We enjoyed them all. How grand that three-story hotel is! I especially like the view of the railway station and the wagons lined up ready to load the barrels of potatoes onto the boxcars. Ray was particularly interested in the new modern potato digger pulled by four mules. He said he'd like to have that this fall! Thanks very much for sending the cards.*

*Ray has been very busy this week—giving the hogs worm medicine, putting smoke under the hams, drawing manure, putting up nineteen barrels of corn, etc.*

*I worked on my apple piece some more, made a black calico dress skirt, and read a good book which Mrs. Clarke loaned me—'Around the World for Sixty Dollars.'*

*It is clear and warmer today. The snow is starting to melt. A cutter slid into the ditch near here this afternoon. The man and his wife asked to leave their horse in our barn until they can get their cutter repaired tomorrow. They had to walk to Wilton to catch the car to Glens Falls.*

*The first auto of the season passed by here. I hope it didn't end in the ditch also.*

*Ray is very upset about the Luick's dog. It has chased our chickens ever since they moved into Jo Henry's shanty last month. Today it hurt two hens. I am afraid Ray will kill the dog if it comes back again.*

*I do hope you can come and spend some time here on the farm this summer. The Nix Company will give you a vacation, won't they? My thoughts are always with you.*

*Lovingly,*
*Mother*

On March 15th Lottie was thrilled to learn that Grace's baby had come the day before. It was a son weighing ten pounds, born at four o'clock in the morning. She could hardly wait to see him, but the hard rain forced her to wait until Saturday. In preparation for the big event, she had already given Grace a hand-embroidered crib blanket. Now she set to work making an applecake for them.

While it was baking, she began on Harold's clover painting. He wouldn't be critical, so she wouldn't spend as much time on his picture. She put in the outline of the round green bowl with a mass of red clover spilling over in all directions onto her good lace tablecloth. Humming as she worked, she thought about Harold and his bunch of clover. He had crept in with his pathetic monkey-crawl last summer and handed her a large bunch of clover.

"Here, Gramma, I picked these for you. Put 'em on the table f'r a middlepiece," he had said.

Lottie thought about how much that little gesture had meant to her because it had taken so much effort on Harold's part. He had been barely five years old then, and he had dragged himself along the ground, picking the red clover out in the field. He had crushed as many plants as he had picked flowers, sitting on them while he reached for more blossoms. No one would have dreamed of chiding him for that though. Lottie was glad he had asked her to paint the clover. It made her feel again so strongly the warm glow his gift had given her.

Ray came in from the barn just then, elated with more happy news.

"Blossom just had her lamb, Ma. It's a buck!"

"Oh, that's grand! A buck, eh? I'll go see him when the rain stops. We'll have to think of a name for him. What did you say the Myers named their baby?"

"They named him Donald."

When Stanley's divorce became final, Lottie exulted. At last he was free of Lulu. Lottie had never cared for her, although she had tried to be kind. Now she was impatient to hear what Stanley was going to do now. He hadn't referred to Hortense in some time. Was he tired of her, or was he waiting for the divorce to be final before asking her to marry him? Perhaps she had found another man in the meantime. At any rate, Lottie was determined not to ask any more personal questions. Why should a mother have a right to ask any more questions than a friend would? She would just have to wait and see.

Her apprehension about Stanley was probably just the imagination of a silly old woman, she decided. After all, what could happen? The worst thing Lottie could envision would be for Stanley to marry another woman just like Lulu, and that wouldn't be anything new at all.

# THE NEW FIANCEE
## Chapter 4

It was a cloudy, rainy Sunday, the last day of March, but it turned out to be one of the most exciting days of the year for Charlotte Bush. Clifford had written that he had a bag of English potatoes to bring Ray, so he and Harold would come in time for dinner. Clif had cautioned Harold not to tell Grandma what else they were bringing, so for once they arrived quietly. Clif brought in the big box and waited for his mother's reaction. He hadn't written her that it had come from the factory, but waited to surprise her.

When she saw the box, she clapped her hands like a delighted child. She was so excited she could hardly stand still while Clif unpacked it and set it on the table. It was her very own gramophone! He cranked up the machine and immediately a cheerful melody filled the room.

"Oh, you beautiful doll—you great, big beautiful doll. Let me put my arms around you. . . ." the big blue speaker sang out clearly.

"Aren't you s'prised, Gramma?" Harold was glad he could talk now. "Pa and me had a secret, and I didn't tell. Do you like it, Gramma?"

"Oh, yes, Harold. It's the grandest thing ever!"

Lottie was so excited she could hardly keep from bursting. Now she had her own talking machine. Harold began stamping the floor. He didn't try to sing along with the record this time, but he kept the rhythm with his feet clumping awkwardly.

In a few minutes Lottie remembered the painting, and she brought it and set it beside the gramophone. Harold looked up and shouted, "My Bunch of Clover! Thank you, Gramma. Oh, that's beautiful! Just what I wanted! C'n I take it home with me when we go?"

"I'm so glad you like it, Harold. Of course you can take it home with you. It might be best not to touch the paint for a few days until it's quite dry, though. Your Pa can help you carry it so the paint won't smudge."

"That's just the way it looked—you had the green bowl on the dining room table and the lace tablecloth. You 'member, don't you, Gramma?"

"Yes, I certainly do."

"Look, Pa! Did you see my painting that Gramma painted f'r me?"

"Yes, Harold. That's beautiful. Grandma's a good artist, isn't she?"

"She's the bestest artist I ever saw," he said emphatically.

Lottie smiled, wondering if Harold had ever seen any other artist.

The record ended, and Clif put another one on. Lottie was so proud of her new graphophone! She watched the blue speaker raptly as it poured forth, "I want a girl just like the girl that married dear old Dad. . . ."

"Wouldn't your Pa have enjoyed this wonderful machine!" she exclaimed. "I wonder what they'll invent next. There couldn't be anything nicer than this!"

Ray had become much more self-sufficient in the past year. Before that he had been like a hired man on his father's farm. Even when George had become too ill to oversee the work, Ray had still reported to him on each day's progress, like a dutiful son. When Ray became the overseer at his father's death, he was well trained and capable. Only after several weeks as his own boss, did his self-esteem begin to grow with the realization that Ma trusted and respected him, just as she had trusted and respected Pa. His self-confidence increased when he found that Ma wasn't giving him orders, but was accepting him as the man who made the decisions.

For the first time in his life Ray was free to be himself and to feel a sense of power. His older brother, Clifford, was seldom around to give him a feeling of youth and inferiority. His younger brother, Stanley, was far away where his infernal talking and simpering couldn't plague him. He found himself hoping again that Stanley would stay permanently in Florida.

34

He did wish for some of Florida's warm weather on his shopping trip to Glens Falls in the wagon though. There was a wind from the northeast sweeping down the Hudson Valley from Canada and it was terribly cold, although it was the second week in April. When he came in half frozen from the nine-mile trip, Lottie poured him a cup of hot tea to warm him up, while he hung up his ulster, hat, and muffler.

"It looks like snow again, Ma. I think you put your furs away too soon. I don't know when I'll get the potatoes in the ground, if it stays this cold. You'll be wanting to plant your sweet peas too. Everything'll be late this year."

"Well, we can't help that. One day spring will be here. It'll be an extra good summer, to make up for winter lasting so long," she predicted with her usual philosophical attitude.

Lottie was appalled when she found out Ray had spent $32.05, but she knew those were necessary expenditures. Carefully she entered the items in her diary: seeds, turpentine, castor oil, harness, and green paint for the blinds. It was businesslike, she thought, having a notation as to who had paid for eggs or butter or hay, what Pratt had paid for their hogs and cows, and how much they paid for their supplies. Neatness and order in everything was very important to Lottie.

A few days later Ray brought the news that Mrs. Myers, John's mother, had fallen and broken her hip. The good news was that the weather suddenly turned warm and the snow vanished from most of the yard.

Lottie took advantage of the change in the weather to walk down to the Myers to visit. Mrs. Price, who had come to help in the perturbed household, opened the door and ushered her into the big dining room. Lottie was a little out of breath from her unaccustomed walk. She untied the apron she had put over her head. It was the first time this spring that she had walked the quarter of a mile between the houses. Setting the preserves and the applecake she had brought on the dining room table, she went over to the cot where Mrs. Myers was lying.

"Oh, Frances, I'm so sorry to hear about your leg. Are you in a lot of pain?"

"Yes, I'm absolutely miserable," moaned the old lady. "I didn't

35

sleep at all last night. The doctors are coming back tomorrow to put a cast on my leg."

"You'll feel more comfortable then, I hope."

Lottie glanced around the dining room.

"I suppose this is to be your bedchamber until your leg has healed. You wouldn't be able to climb the stairs."

"That's right, and I must remain here in everyone's way at least eight weeks." She groaned pitifully.

Just then Grace came in carrying the baby.

"My, hasn't Donald grown!"

"He's almost a month old now, and such a good baby. He's really a joy to us all."

"May I hold him for a few minutes, Grace dear?"

"Of course you may. Here, put this blanket in your lap first."

Mrs. Myers looked at the baby longingly. "I was going to hold him yesterday, when I fell. Now I'll be lying here for weeks not even able to pick up my own grandson," she said plaintively.

Lottie chatted for a long while, telling Mrs. Myers and Grace all the news she could think of. Then she mentioned as casually as possible that Stanley's divorce was finalized two weeks ago.

When they questioned her about Stanley's intentions for the future, she admitted she didn't know, but he had met a lady named Hortense Estes who was a sales clerk in Hastings. She didn't want to talk about the woman who seemed to her at this distance like Lulu's twin.

Charlotte Bush read a great deal, and her language tended to be in a very literary style. She looked and spoke like an erudite professor who loved to talk. With two shut-ins here to listen, she was set to lecture all afternoon. Suddenly she realized that she had been discoursing too long and it was getting late.

"Dear friends, I've been a prattling old woman. Please forgive me for disturbing you for such a long time. Frances, I hope you'll feel better soon. Grace, your dear baby has slept this whole hour, lulled by the dullness of my converstion. He's a darling child."

As she trotted back home with her apron over her head again, Lottie felt especially grateful for her two good legs. She was ecstatic at the hint of spring in the air. The winter had been so severe and confining for her that it was really marvelous to be out walking in the fresh air again. She could hardly wait for planting time. Ray would plant the vegetables there beside the barn, and she would plant flowers beside the house.

Before long the green bowl on the dining room table would be filled with flowers again. First would come dainty, pastel sweet peas, then blush pink apple blossoms, creamy white roses from the bush behind the house, and later marigolds, zinnias, gladiolus, and the crimson clover that Harold loved. In the fall there would be asters, golden glow, and chrysanthemums.

As she turned into the yard she looked toward the mountain, where a few patches of snow shone through the trees. One of its loveliest times is coming soon when the new spring pale greens contrast so dramatically with the dark green of the hemlocks, she thought. She spoke aloud.

"Thank you, Lord, for spring. I think I like it best of all the seasons."

It was only a few days later that the news Lottie had been expecting—and dreading—came in the mail. Stanley wrote that he was engaged to Hortense Estes.

Lottie hoped this would work for Stanley's happiness, but she dreaded another mistake. What kind of woman was Hortense Estes? She knew Stanley's capacity for exaggeration. Hortense couldn't possibly be as beautiful, sweet, and wonderful as he said she was. She wouldn't be human. Lottie hoped she wouldn't be as stupid, vain, and useless as Ray thought she was. Could Stanley have been lucky enough to find a warm, kindly person somewhere in between the two? Someone with a pleasant disposition? Lottie tried to picture a mature, nice-enough looking, thirtyish woman; a calm, settled person who could mother Stanley a little and quiet his restless, nervous spirit. Somehow she couldn't fix an image in her mind. Ray's description of the empty-headed dancing girl kept getting in the way. Well, there was nothing she could do about it. Nobody could tell Stanley anything. If he had made up his mind to marry Hortense, they would just have to make the best of it, even if they hated her.

Ray was devastated. There had been a moment of elation, when Ma read the letter aloud, but the fourth sentence was a calamity as far as Ray was concerned.

"Hortense and I plan to be married middle of June. Probably build a house here in Hastings later on. Nix doesn't need as much help in summer—said I could have rest of summer off. We'll come to Saratoga and have a glorious honeymoon! Have to be back after Labor Day. . . ."

All summer! How could he stand it? Clif's prediction had been right. Ray went out and slapped whitewash on the henhouse as furiously as if he had been painting Stanley. Then he whitewashed the hams bags to keep away the flies. When he was upset or angry he found a great deal of solace in rigorous labor.

Of course Lottie wrote Stanley that his plan was fine with her. She congratulated him and hoped that he and Hortense would be very happy. They would be welcome to stay all summer on the farm. There was always plenty of food, and they could use Stanley's help with the many summer chores. He could take Hortense sightseeing from here. She assured him that she was anxious to meet Hortense and see for herself how beautiful his fiancee was.

As she wrote these cordial words, she privately wondered whether there would be any peace at "The Gables" this summer. Could she put on a pretense of liking someone she detested for three months? Could Ray be civil to her—and especially to Stanley—all summer?

It was time to start the spring housecleaning. Lottie was a meticulous housekeeper, but in the spring she went into a frenzy that would have exhausted a woman half her age. The winter weather outside and wood and coal smoke inside were hard on a house. She would spend the next two months systematically sprucing up the house—scrubbing, painting, varnishing, tidying, and regulating. In her diligence she wore out her broom, made callouses on her knees, got whitewash in her hair, and varnish under her fingernails. This year she had a special incentive to make it look extra nice for the new bride. She set to work humming, "Let me call you sweetheart, I'm in love with you. . . ."

That's it! she realized suddenly. Stanley's in love with Hortense, whether Ray and I like her or not. If they love each other, that's all that matters. I do hope I'm going to like her though.

Lottie was a truly kind and compassionate person. She intended to do her utmost to help Hortense feel at home. Still she couldn't forget how difficult it had been to be nice to Stanley's first wife. She dreaded meeting his new fiancee and didn't expect to like her.

38

On April 14 came an event that stunned people all across the country, as well as the Bushes. Sunday night the great ship *Titanic* struck an iceberg. Monday's papers reported the ship limping in under its own power—some lifeboats having been launched but not filled. Everyone was sure that the *Titanic* was unsinkable, so why get into one of those little lifeboats? Tuesday's papers came out with the horrifying news that between 1200 and 1400 people had gone down with the ship at 3:00 a.m. Monday.

On Wednesday Emma Green spent the afternoon with Lottie. They discussed the terrible tragedy in awed tones.

"Isn't it sad!"

"Oh, I'm so sorry for those poor people!"

"Why didn't they fill the lifeboats?"

"Whose fault was it?"

In all the discussions that question came up. Who was to blame for this awful tragedy? When Emma found out that Lottie had only seen the *Saratogian*, she promised to send her the *New York Times*, which had many more details about the disaster.

When Lottie wrote to Stanley, she couldn't get the *Titanic* off her mind, so that was mainly what she wrote about. "Did the news about the *Titanic* appear in your Florida newspapers?" She reiterated her invitation for him to bring his bride to "The Gables" for the summer.

"I am really very curious about Hortense," she wrote, not mentioning all the negative pictures she had imagined. This time she visualized an uneducated wench. Hastings was a small town and probably had few eligible young ladies. In his loneliness, Stanley may have been taken in by some woman of poor moral character, she feared.

She wrote about her spring cleaning progress. It should be all finished by the middle of June, if all went well. She reminded him how lovely the farm and the mountain would be if they could come while spring was still fresh and green.

On Monday morning Jennie Varney had suffered a stroke. Lottie went to see her and was shocked to see her lying there so still, not moving and not knowing anyone.

"My poor friend—such a dear person," she whispered. "How many good visits we've had, and how many happy and sad times we've shared!"

Lottie worried about Jennie while she cleaned and whitewashed the walls and ceiling of the creamery. The two-foot thick stone walls kept the little building delightfully cool in summer, but today it felt frigid and deathlike.

At midnight Jennie Varney died.

One more old friend gone, thought Lottie. Soon it'll be my turn. I'm glad she didn't linger as a helpless invalid in pain and discomfort any longer. How terrible that would have been for her if she had remained paralyzed and unable to speak or do anything for herself! I hope I never have to lie in bed like that, not aware of anything, and being such a burden to my family.

There were many mourners at the funeral on Sunday. Weeping together united the community in its grief. After the service at the Varney home, wagons and buggies formed a procession for the long trip to the cemetery at Gurn Spring, four miles away.

Ray dipped the lambs the next Saturday, pushing them into an arsenic solution in the big arch kettle to kill sheep-ticks, and other vermin. It was essential for the health of the animals, but Ray was upset when it resulted in the death of a lamb, as occasionally happened. This time one of Cinnamon's lambs died, despite all he could do to try to save it.

"Poor little devil," he muttered. "There ought to be a better way to get rid of ticks."

Big, tough Ray wept as he buried the tiny limp form.

Jennie Varney's death had moved him deeply. At the funeral he had thought that it might have been Ma lying there in the casket—Ma struck down suddenly by a crippling, killing stroke.

Now this dear little lamb that had been leaping and cavorting just moments before he dipped it was dead. How precarious life is! He hated the thought that he had been responsible for the poor creature's death.

"You couldn't help it, dear," he imagined his wife consoling him. She would hug and kiss him until the tears subsided.

Next day Ray put in the first peas of the season. His nose quivered at the thought of the bittersweet odor of fresh pea pods. Nothing could compare with fresh vegetables pulled from the plants in the morning and cooked and eaten that same day. He could hardly wait for these dried, wrinkled little peas to produce food for his dinner. It would be about the end of June before they would be ready to pick, he figured.

Then he planted half a bushel of new potatoes.

Peas and new potatoes, thought Ray, and his stomach purred.

He built a new line fence over the creek. Then walking to the back of the property high up on the mountain, he checked along the way for any breaks in the old fence. While he was mending a place near the back corner, he heard the wind begin to murmur in the tall pines, and he stopped to listen. The murmur became a soft sigh, then a gentle singing and it soared in a delicate crescendo to an exquisite symphony of sound. One of the greatest joys of the winter to him was the music of the pines. When the hardwoods leafed out in their new spring green and began their noisy rustling, he would no longer be able to hear the subtle music of the pines. Ray was a rough man with no talent for music, but his whole being felt in tune with nature's songs.

Now his thoughts turned again to the devoted wife he yearned for so desperately. He could share moments of beauty like this with her. Somehow it didn't seem right to go into the house where Ma was sweeping and scrubbing so diligently, and say, "Ma, you should go out on the mountain and listen to the wind in the pines." He could imagine her thinking he had gone quite daft. But a sensitive, understanding wife would say, "Oh, Ray, I would love to come with you and hear it!" And she would link her arm in his and skip along the path to share the little pleasures that he enjoyed so much.

It was an especially pleasant spring. Except for his need of a wife, Ray was really quite content. But now Stanley was coming! Oh, Blazes! With a silly, stupid floozy, too! His contented mood changed abruptly to wretchedness.

# SARATOGA SPRING
## Chapter 5

Clifford had sent Ray a note saying that he had sixty-four barrels ready for him at fifteen cents per barrel. When May finally brought some fair weather, Ray went to Corinth to pick them up.

Harold was "helping" his father at the store when Ray went in.

"Hello, Uncle Ray!" he yelled in his usual boisterous voice, delighted to see his beloved uncle.

The enthusiastic little boy proceeded to try to sell Uncle Ray several products that were popular with the townspeople of Corinth and Palmer, but which Ray and Lottie didn't need on the farm. Harold couldn't read yet, but he could identify many of the items by their packaging.

"Look at this Fairy soap—it fits your hand and only costs five cents," he said eagerly.

"Harold, you know we make our own soft soap on the farm," Ray objected.

"Well, how 'bout some shredded wheat?" wheedled Harold.

"I don't think so, Harold. We've got plenty of oatmeal for breakfast."

"Here's a nice little can of Log Cabin syrup. See what a cute can it is—it looks like a real log cabin!" Harold was determined to sell him something.

"That's nice, but I think Grandma would say it's too dear. It'll be cheaper for me to buy the gallon jug for ninety cents. Then we'll have plenty when you come to visit us."

That idea appealed to him.

"Okay, Uncle Ray."

Harold struggled manfully to lift the big jug and take it to his father to put on Ray's bill.

He was managing his brace better now. He could walk a little faster, but his gait was rolling and stiff-legged. He used his stomach muscles to lift each leg and swing it around for every step.

When Ray had all the barrels stacked up on the big lumber wagon, it looked too heavy to budge. Delmar and Alban glanced over their shoulders at the load they were expected to pull. The empty barrels weren't really too heavy though. Ray let the horses poke along on the way back over the mountain, while he enjoyed the warm sunshine. The new little green buds were beginning to pop open on some of the earliest trees. The maple blossoms looked quite red against the blue sky. He needed to share his feeling of elation with someone.

"Look, dearest," he said to the wife he fancied was by his side, "the maple trees are the heralds of spring. Isn't that tree beautiful? If you like, I'll climb the tree and cut some branches to put on the table at home."

That evening there was a pleasant social time at the Epworth League affair. It was the first opportunity for neighbors and friends to get together, except for the funeral. The church members took up a collection to make up the deficiency in last year's salary to the minister. Luckily contributions were generous, and they even had $2.50 left over.

On Monday Ray plowed his oat field, pulverizing the soil, manure, and bits of straw all together, as well as the pesky and irrepressible ferns that grew everywhere. He could visualize the pale green spikes popping through the ground and gradually changing the dark brown field to a soft, undulating sea of green.

Ray loved all the seasons and found something good in every day of the year. But in the spring he felt in harmony with all of nature, as each plant responded to the sun's warmth and surged up to meet it. Alban plodded steadily along with only the slightest tug when it was time to change direction at the end of every row.

Seated on the harrow with the sun caressing his back, Ray felt supremely contented. He imagined that same delicious warm feeling with a woman cuddling next to him in bed on a cold winter night. He would say, "Are you comfortable, Eve, dear?" and she would press her body close to him and purr happily. She would run her hands over his arm and shoulder muscles and say, "You're so strong and wonderful, darling." He would touch her soft body ever so gently, remembering that his hands were rough, and she would respond by drawing him even closer and whispering, "I love you," in his ear.

Just as he was about to become passionate, Alban made the next turn without Ray's command, and he roused from his daydream. If only he had a sweet, affectionate wife, everything would be perfect. Ma was aging; she wouldn't live forever to cook and keep house for him—what would he do when she died, if he hadn't found a wife in the meantime?

Stanley had found a wife. Oh, damn! He hadn't wanted to think about that. Soon Stanley would be here to spend the summer. As if that weren't bad enough, there would be his wife too—an empty-headed party girl who wouldn't like anything about their farm life.

"I hope Hortense doesn't like it here and refuses to stay," he said aloud. "I don't think I can stand having her and Stanley here all summer."

He knew that was a selfish thought, but he couldn't help it. He just didn't like Stanley and was positive he wouldn't like his new wife either. Maybe Hortense would hate the farm and insist on staying in one of those swank hotels in Saratoga.

Lottie had written to Stanley on Sunday, wishing him a happy birthday. It was hard to realize that her "baby" was thirty-four years old today. How long had he been a worry to her? She was so proud when Stanley enlisted in May of 1898 and put on his uniform. The anxiety came later, after the troops were moved to Florida and were scheduled to go to Cuba. Only after he wrote in a shaky hand that he was recovering from malaria at the army camp on Tampa Bay, and wouldn't be going into battle after all, did his mother begin to relax.

Now Lottie was thankful that he had survived both the war and the malaria. After Stanley mustered out of the army, he went to work in Glens Falls. Later he married Lulu Howe and seemed happy for a while, gallivanting and partying all the time. But he was fired from one job after another; he and Lulu quarreled—about what Lottie never knew—and finally he took a job that sent him a thousand miles or more from home.

When she saw him next, he would be married to Hortense. She began to try again to guess what Hortense would be like. This time she pictured a brittle, painted shop girl she had seen once in New York, with a harsh voice and a superior air. Would Stanley have considered that girl "beautiful and sweet?"

Would she be able to accept such a woman as her daughter-in-law? No one in the family had ever liked his first wife. They treated her politely, but there was no warmth in their relationship. Would it be just as difficult to be friendly with the brash, loud-mouthed creature she was picturing now? Could she possibly learn to love this hussy she imagined Hortense to be? Even though she was dreading meeting the woman, her curiosity compelled her to wish the time for their visit would come sooner. Suspense was a hard companion.

On Wednesday Lottie was so miserable with indigestion that Ray went into the village and brought Dr. Roods to see her.

"Mrs. Roods is complaining of the same thing," he said jovially as he doled out some pills.

On Thursday Lottie felt much better and took up the butter after Ray had churned, then packed it into jars and cleaned the churn. But Friday she was worse, and Saturday Ray had to go after Dr. Roods again. He gave her some pills that seemed to help this time, and she paid him $2.00 for the two visits and the pills.

When Clif and his family came, she perked up and forgot to feel sick. They gave her some new records by Caruso and John McCormack, but her favorite was "Redwing." Soon the lilting music had her humming along.

"Oh, I'm dreaming tonight of pretty Redwing. . . ."

When Ray came in with the mail, her spirits soared even higher. Stanley had sent a picture of the office force sitting on the steps of the small frame building that was his office in Hastings.

"Look, Clifford!" she exclaimed. "Look what a grand picture this is! Look, Mary! Stanley's quite the handsomest man in the picture, don't you think?"

"Let me see!" demanded Harold.

He swung each leg forward and clumped noisily until he reached Lottie's chair. His walk was still painful to watch.

"Which one's Uncle Stanley?"

"Can't you tell, dear? Don't you recognize him?"

"No, I don't 'member him, Ma. Which one is he?"

"This one, Harold—in the front row on the right. I guess it's been a long time since you saw him."

45

"Is Uncle Stanley nice?"

"Of course he is, dear. He'll be here soon with Hortense, who'll be his wife."

"Is Hortense nice?"

"She must be nice or Uncle Stanley wouldn't have fallen in love with her. She'll be your Aunt Hortense."

Harold noticed the bowl of maple blossoms on the table and remembered his picture.

"Oh, Gramma, I hanged the 'Bunch of Clover' you gived me over my bed," he announced proudly.

"That's nice, Harold. I'm sure it looks pretty there."

He nodded solemnly. "It looks real pretty there." He paused and then inquired greedily, "What's for supper, Gramma?"

"We're going to have some nice vegetable soup."

"Is it Campbell's soup?"

Harold had spent so much time in the store that he was very brand name conscious.

"No, Dear. It's Grandma's own homemade soup, made from all the good vegetables we grew in the garden last summer. Do you remember helping us pick them?"

Harold looked glum. "Yes, I 'member, but I don't like vege'bles much. I don't wanna eat that." He hesitated, then asked, "What's f'r dessert?"

"It's baking in the oven now. Can you smell it?"

"I think I smell pie plant," he said finally.

"You're absolutely right. It's rhubarb pie."

Harold liked that and he liked strawberry shortcake too. They had that for dinner the next day, made with the strawberries Clif had brought, and extra large biscuits, with plenty of fresh, sweetened whipped cream.

Sunday was Mother's Day. Lottie was especially glad the children had come for the weekend. They made a fuss over her and made her glad to be a mother. She was happiest when her children were gathered around her and she was cooking huge farm meals for them. Putting more and more food on the table was an expression of love for her family.

While they were eating dinner, Clifford asked his mother a question she couldn't answer.

"Ma, what d' you think Hortense is like? I can't figure her out from Stanley's letters, c'n you?"

46

"No, Son. All I know is he says she's beautiful and sweet and wonderful. She has brown eyes and brown hair. She works in the general store at Hastings, so she must be fairly independent, but certainly not wealthy. For the life of me, I can't figure out why she isn't living in St. Petersburg, where her parents live. Stanley says she lives with her cousin, Lilly, and her cousin runs the store—or rather her cousin's husband runs it."

"It's hard to decipher Stanley's letters, isn't it? He writes a lot, but he doesn't say much. Do you know where they'll be married?"

"I suppose they'll go to St. Petersburg. Surely her parents will want to have the wedding there."

Clifford winked at Mary and got up to put a record on the talking machine.

"Down by the old mill stream, where I first met you . . ." sang the big blue speaker.

"That's my fav'rite song," Mary explained with a smile.

When Clif and his family left, Lottie gave them all the asparagus that was above ground. It made a nice fat bundle.

After they had gone, Ray turned the sheep out into the orchard for the first time. He had put a fence across a bubbling creek there, so the sheep would have running water. In a few weeks he would rotate them to another spot along the creek. They began nibbling happily at the fresh grass.

During a rainy spell in the middle of May there was a commotion in the road near the barn. Milo Grey was gesturing and pointing, walking back and forth from the center of the road to the ditch. He was explaining to two other men what had happened last Tuesday when he had his auto smash there in front of Jo Henry's shanty. It had rained a lot the day before, and the road was very slippery and muddy. He didn't have the new non-skid tires either.

"Autos are dangerous!" was Lottie's comment when Ray reported the news. "I've seen people zipping by here at over twenty miles an hour! I feel much safer behind a good horse."

"Just as well you do, Ma. We can't afford an auto, anyway. The best bargain I've seen advertised is the Ford, and it's $690. I don't know how anybody can afford one."

He held up the new wallpaper he had just brought in from Van Rensselaer's store.

47

"Oh, good—I'm glad it finally came. As soon as I finish moving into the big kitchen for the summer, I'll paper the den. I need to scrub the ceiling and paint the floor too. Everything looks so grimy! When I clean one room it makes the rest of the house look even shabbier. There's so much yet to do. I don't think I can get all the spring cleaning done before Stanley and Hortense get here. That's only a month from now! I do so want everything to look especially nice when they come."

"Why does it matter, Ma? Stanley can help you with the painting and varnishing when he gets here."

"I know he wouldn't mind, but I want to make a good first impression on his bride. Besides, Stanley shouldn't have to start painting the minute he gets here on his honeymoon!"

Ray grunted. "Probably a waste of time trying to make a good impression on *her!*" His resentment of Stanley's impending visit was growing stronger as the time approached.

Lottie pursed her lips. She knew Ray didn't expect to like Hortense any more than she did.

"Now, Ray, you must be nice to Hortense," she admonished. "She's probably a very nice lady," but she didn't believe her own words. Lottie was getting uneasy about the approaching visit, but what could possibly happen, aside from the almost certain knowledge that they weren't going to like Hortense?

One lovely spring day the Myers walked over, carrying their baby for his first visit.

"My goodness, how Donald has grown! He must weigh fifteen pounds! Such a fine, healthy boy—John, I believe he looks like you."

"Does that mean I look like a baby?"

Everyone laughed.

"How's your Ma, John?"

"I don't think she's any better, thank you, Ray. I hate to say it, but it looks like she won't ever walk again."

"Now, Rip, don't be discouraged," put in Grace. "It's only been six weeks, and Dr. Roods said it would take at least that long for the hip to mend. She'll be better soon."

It was the custom whenever neighbors got together to discuss current events. They were country people, but they could still be well-informed, and they all devoured every word in the newspaper each day.

"Grace, how do you feel about the parades the suffragists have had in Albany and New York?" Ray inquired.

"I'm in favor of woman suffrage, Ray, but I'm opposed to any violent means of getting it. I certainly hope we won't have anything in this country like the window smashing and riots they've had in England. . . ."

Ray interrupted, "Of course those riots in London were terrible, but I think the police were wrong to force-feed the suffragettes."

"Those poor women." clucked Lottie. "It was most unfair to injure them just because they refused to eat while in prison!"

Grace continued, "I suppose peaceful parades, meetings, and speeches are all right, if the women have no family to care for. But I really believe that a woman's place is in the home, taking care of her husband and family."

She smiled at John. He reached over and patted her hand.

"Well spoken, my dear. How do you feel about it, Lottie?"

"I'm so old now—I guess I'm too old to learn how to vote, and certainly not interested in parading. George and I always talked over the candidates before an election. Then he voted for both of us, and I see nothing unfair about that. Now that he's gone— well, that makes a difference. If I were young I suppose I'd be anxious to get the vote."

"Lottie, you're a very well read and highly intelligent person. A man has to pass a literacy test in order to register to vote. If you can pass that test too, why shouldn't you have the same right? Look at my wife here—she's taught the boys who'll grow up and get the vote when they're twenty-one, but she can't vote herself!" John really sounded quite angry about it.

"It's only through education that children have a chance in life. If all children are taught to read, write, and think for themselves, then why shoudn't they all have the same right to vote for their political leaders? I'm sure some day they will."

"You're such a fine teacher, Grace. I've heard that you inspired many young people to improve their lives by studying hard and going on to get as much education as possible. Do you think you'll go back to teaching when Donald is older?"

"I doubt it, Lottie. When he's older I hope to have another

49

baby—a little girl would be nice. The greatest contribution I can make now is to be a full time wife and mother."

John was sitting straight and tall, bursting with pride in his lovely wife.

"She's really making a great contribution, I'd say!"

"I think so too," Lottie agreed, smiling at the sleeping baby.

"What's the latest news from Stanley?"

When Lottie had told them all about Stanley's plans to bring his bride to Saratoga for the summer, Grace said enthusiastically, "Then we'll get to see her for ourselves! How wonderful! Is she about Stan's age?"

There was a momentary pause, as Ray and Lottie glanced at each other.

"We don't know how old she is," Lottie confessed. "We assume she must be around thirty or so—Stanley's thirty-four, you know. He's never said anything about her age."

"Maybe she's sensitive about her age, as some women are, and didn't want him to tell you."

"Or maybe she's older than he is," John suggested.

That was a new thought for Lottie. An older woman might be just what Stanley needed. The more she thought about it the more she liked the idea. She began imagining a matronly woman with a jolly disposition.

Lottie heard Harold shouting before Clif's wagon turned into the yard the following Sunday.

"Gramma, Gramma! Guess what happened to me!"

"What happened, Harold?" she asked anxiously, as she hurried to meet them at the side steps.

"I fell down on the whiffle tree!"

"Oh, my goodness, Harold. How did that happen?"

"Billy stopped, and I fell down on the whiffle-tree." he said, as if that explained it all.

Clifford was shaking and his face was white.

"Ma, you know how Billy stops suddenly sometimes on those humps in the mountain road? You know how he always kicks the whiffle tree every time he stops? Well, he stopped so suddenly that Harold lost his balance and fell over the dashboard and onto the whiffle tree. I thought sure he'd be killed. I yelled at Billy as loud as I could. This is the only time I've ever known him not to kick the whiffle-tree. We're real lucky, I tell you."

"I'm certainly thankful for that, Clifford."

"I don't know what I'll do, but I'm going to have to get rid of Billy," Clif muttered.

Lottie turned to Harold and said, "I'm so glad you weren't hurt, dear." She gave him a hug.

"I'm glad I weren't hurt too, Gramma."

Clif set the boxes of groceries up on the porch. Then he reached back in the wagon and pulled out a huge bunch of lilac and tulip blossoms and presented them to his mother. They were the first Lottie had seen this year. She buried her nose in the flowers, appreciatively breathing in the distinctive fragrance of the lilacs. Clif handed Ray a bundle of healthy-looking tomato plants. Ray admired the plants even more than his mother admired the flowers. Clif was thoughtful and considerate. He always brought presents when he came to the farm—and they were always well chosen and appropriate.

Lottie said, "Here, Harold, why don't you carry these flowers in for me, while I carry some of the groceries. Goodness, we have a lot of groceries this time!"

She picked up a box and left the others for Ray to bring while Clifford took Billy to the barn.

In the kitchen she unpacked the boxes. "Let's see—tea, coffee, baking powder, candles, vinegar, canning jars and rubber sealing rings, chocolate, and a twenty-five pound bag of sugar. I think that's everything I ordered. And here are strawberries, candy, and oranges too!"

"Those are a gift for you, Ma," Clif told her.

"Thank you, Dear. We have 20 dozen eggs for you to take back to the store with you—they're worth twenty cents a dozen."

"That's a fair swap. Your groceries came to $4.00 even."

Harold had gone clumping down the steps and was out by the barn watching Ray plant the tomatoes.

"You make things grow good, Uncle Ray. When I grow up I wanna be a farmer like you."

Ray eyed Harold's brace and wondered whether he'd ever be able to do the heavy work involved in farming.

"That's fine," he said. "Keep watching and helping on the farm and some day maybe you'll be a farmer."

He took his buckets and walked down to the barn for some water to pour around the tomato plants. Harold tried to follow

51

him, but it was hard to walk on the uneven ground. He fell head-long when his foot went into a soft furrow. Getting up again was a problem. He was fighting tears of frustration, when Ray came back and helped him up.

"I hate this brace" Harold spluttered, with all the vehemence he could muster through his choked-back tears.

"I don't blame you, Harold. I would too. I think you're a real spunky little guy, though. You're doing just fine with your brace, and some day maybe you won't need it any more."

They went in and washed for dinner. Ray cranked up the Victrola and put on "Alexander's Ragtime Band" to try to cheer Harold up a little. Harold tried to march to the music, but he couldn't keep up. Fortunately Lottie called them to dinner just then. He sat down at the table and beat time with his fists on the table.

"I just don't know what to do about Billy," Clif said gloomily while they were eating. "I'm afraid to let Harold ride with him again. He's a good horse for the store deliveries and we have to have a horse. I can't afford to buy another one myself, and I know the Diedrichs won't want to. He really belongs to them—I don't have the right to sell him. What am I going to do?"

Lottie was a problem solver. She believed in looking at a problem from all angles and trying by all possible means to find a solution. She sat there looking thoughtful for a moment.

"Why don't we take Billy for a while, and you take Delmar? He's a gentle horse and a good worker. I'm sure he could learn the delivery route quickly."

"Yeah, Pa!" Harold clapped his hands. "Delmar's a good horse."

"Ma, that's a wonderful idea! Billy's worked with Alban before. They get along all right together. Delmar *is* very gentle. I'm sure the Diedrichs won't object to a temporary swap, until Harold is bigger."

"Of course they won't. We can swap back again in a few months or a year maybe."

So when Clif hitched up the store wagon to go home, it was Delmar that pulled it instead of Billy. Billy would have to pay for his mischief by working on the farm for the next few months.

Lottie wrote a long letter to Stanley and told him all about Harold's adventure and the swapping of the horses. She asked him to be sure to notify her when they would be arriving in Wilton, so she and Ray could meet the newlyweds with the buggy.

"Is the wedding to be in St. Petersburg? I presume Hortense's parents will want to have it there, of course. . . ."

June was here already, and the spring cleaning was nowhere near finished! Lottie worked energetically, as she had done for the past month. She painted chairs and stairs and porches. Iva Johnson's "patented broom" did a wonderful job of cleaning the carpets and was well worth the quarter to rent it. She was proud of the wallpaper she had put up with flour and water paste. Everything should be clean and neat when Stanley and Hortense arrived.

Now she began wondering if Hortense would be critical and snooty. Would she take one look at the house and then insist that Stanley take her to a hotel in Saratoga Springs rather than spend one night in it?

Somehow it was impossible for Lottie to imagine at this long distance that Hortense was more than just a name. She could never think of Stanley's fiancee as a real person with human emotions and sensitivity. Always her own feelings prevented the realization that Hortense would have feelings too. Her personality, her character, her speech patterns, and her attitudes simply duplicated Lulu's, or whichever objectionable person Lottie was imagining at the moment. Perhaps it was because of Stanley's penchant for choosing noisy, bawdy types as his companions. Lottie rarely liked or respected his friends, although she allowed him to entertain them freely at her home and tactfully never showed her distaste. It never once occurred to her that Stanley's fiancee might have any apprehension about meeting her.

On June 7th the temperature dropped suddenly and Ray became alarmed. He lit the fires in all the orchards late that night and left them smouldering. The apple trees were in full bloom, luminous and ghostly in the darkness. Ray breathed in their delicate fragrance with sensuous pleasure. He stood in the clearing on the mountain and watched the lopsided moon come up. It was well past full, but it shone on the apple blossoms with a haunting beauty. The night was sparkling and crisp, just the kind of weather for a killing frost.

A frost now could be disastrous—could cost them several hundred dollars. He and his mother were very dependent on the money from the apple crop, which showed promise of being especially big this year. While the trees were in full bloom, they were most vulnerable.

He stayed out until quite late, going from the mountain to the ridge and then to the valley where the frost might settle, making sure the fires were all burning well. As usual he felt a need to share the loveliness of this night with someone. He reached out to pull the imaginary woman closer to his side.

"Isn't that beautiful, darling?" he murmured. "I'm glad you came out here with me. It's very cold, but I'll soon get you warm when we go in to bed."

A veil of smoke settled over the trees like a mist. He piled dirt up around each fire to be sure it wouldn't spread and added some green pine branches to make more smoke. Then he went to bed, alone and lonely.

When the sun came up he found no damage, even though there was a heavy frost over on the hill, and the temperature was 31 degrees. Luckily, he had covered his tomato plants with newspapers; the garden seeds were safe in the ground; the grape vines hadn't put out new growth yet; the new pear and peach trees he had just planted were undamaged; and the blossoms on the apple trees were mercifully saved by the protective smoke. Ray felt extremely lucky. His whole apple crop could have been killed, as well as his vegetable garden. Saturday night was cold, but windy and there was no more frost. Summer had pushed Jack Frost back toward the north. It would be a good year—for the crops, at least. But the summer would be miserable for him, with his fat-headed brother and his harlot wife here until Labor Day.

Stanley's next letter said that he and Hortense would be married on June 18, then leave for New York by rail. They would spend two nights in New York City and two in Saratoga Springs, before coming on up to the farm.

Less than a week to finish getting the house ready! Lottie was in a panic. There was still so much to do! She made new curtains for the clothes press, baked, churned, washed, ironed, and regulated as if her life depended on it.

Now the house was gleaming inside and out. Lottie was sure it looked fine enough for Stanley's new bride. Or did it?

It was an old house, perhaps about fifty years old, but had always been cared for lovingly. It had seen many gallons of paint and varnish throughout the years. It was spacious and comfortable, but it was still just an old-fashioned country house. Maybe Hortense would be upset to find that it didn't have a modern indoor bathroom, with a big bathtub and hot water at the turn of a tap. Maybe she would expect to find electric lights and a gas stove in every room. Anyway they wouldn't need the heat in the summer. That was one thing she needn't worry about. Well, if Hortense didn't like their home, it was too bad. Lottie had done the best she could. All she could do now was hope that she would find Hortense congenial. She would do her best to make her feel at home and happy here. But what if Hortense didn't like the farm? What if Hortense didn't like *her*? Lottie wondered if she could spend the whole summer being pleasant and kind to someone who looked down on their simple country ways.

Ray was busy with the hundreds of outside chores. He had hitched Alban up to the horse hoe and was hoeing between the rows of corn and potatoes. When he checked on the potatoes he found bugs, which he pulled off and killed. He inspected the tiny new seedlings of the muskmelons and summer and winter squashes. Better wait another week before planting the red and white beans to climb up the cornstalks, he decided. Next he went to work pulverizing the fields he was going to plant to buckwheat.

The miracle of spring had come to Saratoga County. Mount McGregor was a monochromatic study in myriad shades of green. The farm was at its loveliest. The tender young plants seemed to grow several inches each day, their many shades of green darkening with the sun's caress. Ray looked over the rolling land and felt a deep sense of pride. He had worked hard and, unless some catastrophe occurred, the crops would be plentiful this year. Tiny, pearl-sized apples had already formed; the vineyards were a beautiful sight, curving in neat, orderly green rows along the ridge; the corn spikes were sturdy and almost a foot tall already; the potato foliage was dense and luxuriant; the vegetable garden looked neat and healthy; the new clusters of maple leaves resembled miniature half-furled umbrellas.

It occurred to Ray that Hortense might not consider the farm beautiful, as he did. She might sink a dainty dancing slipper into the rich loam and say, "Ugh, mud!" She might step on tiny new plants, mistaking them for weeds, and turn up her nose at the smell of manure around the barn. The thought spoiled his mood of contentment. How could he possibly be polite to that woman all summer? Without ever seeing her he knew he hated, and would always hate, Hortense Estes Bush.

# THE WEDDING
## Chapter 6

On the twentieth of June two letters came from Stanley. Ray was late bringing home the mail, because he and John Myers had been working together all day. First they had ground the knives of the sheep-shearing machine and then they had sheared very heavy fleeces off the sheep—the buck's fleece alone weighing thirteen pounds. It would take another half day to finish all the Bush's sheep, and then they would start on John's.

Lottie grabbed the letters eagerly and skimmed through the one with an account of the train trip from Jacksonville to Atlanta. The other envelope contained only a quick note asking Ray to meet them in Wilton at 10:30 Sunday morning and a newspaper clipping from *The Atlanta Journal*. As she read, Lottie pictured the wedding as vividly as if she had been there in person.

*The marriage of Miss Hortense Margaret Estes of St. Petersburg, Florida and Mr. Stanley J. Bush, of Saratoga, New York was solemnized Tuesday afternoon at 2:30 o'clock at the home of Mr. and Mrs. W. C. Lawrence on Whitehall Street.*

*The bride wore a gown of white marquisette over white satin and carried bride roses.*

*Little Misses Eleanor and Margaret Lawrence were attractive flower girls, wearing dainty white lingerie dresses, with pink ribbons and carrying pink sweet peas.*

*The ceremony was witnessed by the immediate families and was followed by a buffet luncheon.*

*Mrs. Lawrence was assisted in entertaining by Mrs. E. F. Estes, of St. Petersburg, Florida and Miss Susie Wells.*

*Mr. and Mrs. Bush left immediately after luncheon for New York, Saratoga and other points north. They will make their home in Saratoga during the summer and in Florida for the winter.*

Lottie puzzled over the announcement. "I wonder why they didn't go to St. Petersburg for the wedding. Stanley said Hortense's father wasn't able to go to Atlanta. You'd think they would want to have the wedding in St. Petersburg, so he and their friends could attend."

"I'll tell you why, Ma," Ray said vehemently. "They don't have any friends. That girl had to leave home. She must be some worthless kind of trash. Her father probably refused to give her away. People like that don't have friends."

Lottie was shocked at this outburst from Ray.

"Don't talk like that, Ray. I want you to promise me you won't utter a single unkind word to Stanley or to Hortense all the time they're here. You must be kind and thoughtful of your new sister-in-law. It's a hard thing for her to come here and meet so many strangers. Even if we don't like her, we must never let her know it."

"I promise, Ma," Ray said meekly. "I always try to be nice to Stanley, but he just enrages me with his cocky ways. I promise I'll be kind to Hortense, no matter how much I dislike her."

Even in his promise, Ray was determined that he would never like Hortense.

Ray and Lottie were waiting in the two-seater at the Doe's Corner trolley station, when they heard the 10:30 car come singing in on the rails, with its long arm attached to the overhead wire. Lottie hopped out of the buggy nimbly for her sixty-five years, eager for the first glimpse of her new daughter-in-law. What she saw dumbfounded her. Shock spread across her face first and then immobilized her body.

Ray was angry. That marriage can't possibly last! We should get it annulled! That damn Stanley! How could he do such a thing?

"Ma, is *that* Hortense?" he choked.

"It must be—but that child can't be more than fifteen years old!"

"Oh, my God!" he said under his breath.

The girl stepped timidly and cautiously down from the trolley, glancing back over her shoulder, evidently expecting Stanley to help her. Looking frightened, she stood still at the bottom of the steps, obviously afraid to approach her new in-laws. Stanley was fussing over their valises, bumping and struggling to get them out of the car. While she waited, Hortense shook the wrinkles out of her skirt and smoothed her gloves nervously, looking at them apprehensively with eyes that were too big for her pale face.

If I didn't know Stanley, I would think he was this child's father, Lottie was thinking. What can I possibly say to her? Surely she is too young to be married! Is it too late to have the marriage annulled? They've been together for almost a week! Of all the foolish things Stanley has done, surely this is the worst! I can't imagine what got into him!

Where was the beauty that Stanley had raved so about? Where was the charm that had captivated him and led him to fall in love with her? How could this mouse of a child have taken him in so completely? This could not possibly be the right person for Stanley to spend the rest of his life with!

Lottie forced herself to smile at the girl. She couldn't understand why Hortense should look so terror-stricken over meeting her new in-laws, not realizing how stern and forbidding her own face looked. She didn't know either that the smile looked artificial pasted on her grim visage.

If Ray hadn't been so thunder-struck, he might have stepped forward to help Stanley with the luggage. He stood rooted to the ground, breathing heavily and thinking how he would like to put his hands around Stanley's neck and choke him.

"There's Ma! And Ray!" Stanley chirped, oblivious to Hortense's fright as well as his family's shock.

Beaming and chuckling, Stanley was propelling his bride toward his family to introduce her. He was obviously very pleased with himself and proud of her.

"Ma, I'd like you t' meet the new Mrs. Bush."

Hortense stepped forward with a timid smile. Lottie could see that she was trembling all over, but she spoke bravely in her soft little drawl.

"I'm so happy to meet you at last, Mother Bush."

She almost extended a small, gloved hand to shake Lottie's hand, but noticed that Lottie's fists were clenched tightly.

After a brief hesitation, Lottie recovered enough to welcome Hortense, trying to smile and hide the shock she felt.

When Stanley turned to introduce Hortense to his brother, Ray

stammered, "Pleased to meet you, Hortense," but he thought,
Somehow we've got to find a way to get this girl out of this marriage—it's wrong—it's sinful. Stanley has violated a child! How
could he be such a cad? The poor girl will soon learn what a
mistake she has made and she will be dreadfully unhappy.

Stanley chattered along the way home, pointing out the houses
they passed, happy to be back in Wilton, and wanting his wife to
be happy too. He was completely unaware of his mother's and
brother's reticence.

"There's the Sprott's, where the stagecoach stops, and there's
the Varney's. That's the Myers' House with the columns, and look
at Mount McGregor—see the Eastern Lookout up there where the
grass is?" And with a flourish as they turned into the yard and
pulled up beside the piazza, "Welcome to 'The Gables'."

Now he insisted on taking her for a tour of the large house, up
the front stairway to their large bedchamber and clothes press,
peeking in all the rooms upstairs, then down the back stairway
and through the two kitchens, the big and little dining rooms, the
front and back parlors, the library, and the downstairs bedchamber. He talked constantly, explaining about each room on the
way, wanting her to love the old house just as he did.

Everything intrigued Hortense. Her face was ecstatic. Her eyes
were enormous. That terrible fright had been displaced by excitement.

"This house is so big and ramblin'. It's just like the one in *The
House of the Seven Gables*," she said breathlessly. "Is that why
you call it 'The Gables', Mother Bush?"

"Why, no. I don't know what that is, Hortense."

"It's a book by Nathaniel Hawthorne. I read it in high school."

After an admiring look around the parlor, she said, "Mother
Bush, you're a *wonderful* housekeeper. Everythin' is so neat and
spotless. Stanley told me you put up the wallpaper in the den and
made the quilts I saw upstairs. He said you painted these beautiful
pictures too. You're so talented. I wish I was artistic and smart
like you."

Lottie was more offended than pleased with the compliments,
because she felt that Hortense was insincere and was merely
trying to flatter her. Stanley had made an awful mistake to marry
this young child. Why, she must be only half Stanley's age!

They toured the outbuildings then—the creamery, the "water

60

closet," the carriage house, the shed, the shop, the ice house, the hen house, and the huge red barns across the road. It was a large farm, 137 acres in all. Hortense was enthralled by all she saw, but most of all by the mountain standing like a friendly guard always watching over the farm.

"Can we climb the mountain, Stanley?"

"Sure we can, little lady. Path all the way t' the top. Nice little hike on a clear day."

All the time he was propelling her from room to room and building to building, Stanley had talked incessantly in staccato bursts, rarely making complete sentences. Jabbering. Rattling like a perpetual motion machine. Speaking so fast she couldn't listen fast enough. Trying to show her everything at once. Tell her all about everything. His speech always as crisp as a New York winter.

Hortense was exhausted from trying to absorb it all. It was a relief when Lottie called to them that dinner was ready. They found the big round table loaded with Lottie's usual huge farm dinner and a bowl of creamy white roses in the center. Hortense was too nervous to do more than taste a little of the mashed potatoes and gravy. She was terrified of her stern mother-in-law and her taciturn brother-in-law.

Ray excused himself before the others had finished eating and went outside. He couldn't stand to be around his brother another minute. What in the world could they do about Stanley's seduction of a child? Was it too late for an annulment? he wondered. What about the girl's father? Had he given his consent to her marriage? How could he have been willing to let her marry Stanley if he had met Stanley first? Ray felt sick.

That afternoon Aunt Lydia Staples, Mame King, and Virgie and Perle Kinney motored up to meet Stanley's bride. Everyone wanted to know about the lucky honeymooners' trip up from Georgia.

"What was your favorite part of the trip?" Mame asked, looking at Hortense.

"Why, uh—I guess . . ." she stammered without saying anything intelligible.

She began blushing in embarrassment.

Everyone was looking at her curiously and expectantly. Virgie began to titter. She suspected that Hortense's favorite part of the trip was her new husband's lovemaking in the cramped little pullman berth on the train, in the hotel in New York City, and in the lovely bedroom at the Grand Union in Saratoga Springs.

Lottie made no comment, but her disdain for this shy, inarticulate child was increasing all the time. Maybe she really is stupid, as Ray predicted, she thought.

Stanley covered Hortense's confusion by embarking on a long discourse about the tallest building in the world—the new Woolworth Building, fifty-five stories high—and their subway ride from City Hall to Broadway.

". . . building some new subway lines too," he was saying. "Yessiree, New York City's quite a place. People everywhere. Busiest place in th' world! Went t' see a play on Broadway too."

"What did you see, Hortense?" Virgie asked, trying to give the poor girl another chance to talk.

"We saw *Pirates of Penzance* starring Alice Brady. It was absolutely delightful!" Hortense said, recovering her composure.

"Did you go shopping in the city?" Aunt Lydia asked.

"Oh, yes. I've never seen such elegant department stores before—Macy's and Gimbel's, and especially Lord and Taylor. We stayed at the Astor House and it was just beautiful, but I was so tired from that dirty old train I could have slept on a park bench."

Everyone laughed at the thought of the dainty young girl curled up on a park bench in her long, embroidered dimity frock.

Dr. and Mrs. Roods came in then and got to hear Hortense's glowing account of their two nights in Saratoga Springs.

"You-all should have seen the beautiful room we stayed in at the Grand Union! We went dancin' in their ballroom one night, and the next night we went dancin' at the Casino. Stanley says we can go back there again real soon."

Hortense told how she had loved the elegance of the homes and hotels, the exuberance of the vacationing crowds, and the cool fresh breezes, so different from muggy New York City. She had stood in the empty grandstand at the oldest race track in the United States and imagined the clamor and excitement of the horses thudding around the track.

Stanley beamed at her rapturous recital of the things she had seen. Everyone in the room had been to Saratoga Springs many times, but hearing this young girl's descriptions enchanted all the guests. They were taken with her lilting voice and her slow, deliberate drawl. Her description of the "fizzy" spring water that tickled her nose brought chuckles from the crowd.

Lottie noticed that everyone else seemed to like Hortense and didn't seem concerned about her tender age, but found her delightful and charming. They didn't sense the distress that Lottie felt, or the outrage that Ray felt. Perhaps they didn't take into account how much older Stanley was, Lottie decided.

After the subject of the honeymoon had been exhausted, inevitably the recent break in the Republican party was brought up. Hortense looked from one to another as a lively debate ensued on Teddy Roosevelt and his Progressive party versus President Taft and the Republican party. There was also much speculation as to whom the Democrats would nominate later in the summer.

After many divergent opinions had been expressed, Hortense finally contributed a classic remark, "I think President Taft is much too fat," which brought a burst of laughter.

After everyone else had gone home, still stuffed from a bounteous supper, Lottie dared to ask her new daughter how old she was.

Hortense drew herself up to her full five-foot, one-inch height and replied, "I'm goin' on twenty, Mother Bush. I'll be twenty in September."

Nineteen and married to a thirty-four year old man, thought Lottie. But she's much older than I thought at first.

"I notice the newspaper didn't mention your father at the wedding," she said, hating to appear to pry, but too curious not to ask.

"He couldn't leave the store in St. Petersburg. You see, my sister, Kathleen, lives in Atlanta and she's expectin' a baby in August. She couldn't travel, and my mother wanted to spend the summer with her, so that's why we decided to get married in Atlanta."

"I see," Lottie said, but she really didn't. She felt very strongly that something was wrong. Hortense's father must have opposed the marriage bitterly. Or could there be some truth to the ugly remark Ray had made about Hortense not having any friends? It seemed to her that a wedding in Florida with orange blossoms, being given away by her father, and surrounded by family and friends would have been the normal girl's dream, even if her sister couldn't be there. Was Hortense's father going to try to have the marriage annulled? Or would he do something terrible when he found an opportunity—maybe make trouble for Stanley, or drag his daughter back home? Lottie was sure the girl was holding something back. She seemed much too reluctant to talk about her past. Did she also fear what her father might do?

Hortense lingered in the clothes press that night, until Stanley came in and found her crying despondently. She wept for a long time on his shoulder.

"Your mother doesn't like me," she blurted out.

"Course she does, Tiny. Just doesn't know you very well yet."

"No, I can tell she doesn't approve of me." she said, trying to dry her tears. "All those questions she asked—I know she thinks I was too young to go away from home. She must think I did something dreadful and had to leave home."

"Well, I'll explain. . . ."

"Don't you dare! I don't want anybody to know!"

"Ma will like you just fine when you've been here a few days—you just wait and see."

"I'm goin' to help her with all the housework. That'll make her like me."

"Sure it will, honey."

"I can sweep, set the table, make salad, wash dishes, clean the lamps, but that's not much help, is it?"

"Yes, it is. And you could gather eggs and help Ma with the jelly and such."

"The only trouble is I don't know how to do any real cookin' or sewin' or cleanin', but I can learn!" Her voice was determined.

The next day Stanley volunteered to do the errands and pick up the mail, so he could show Hortense the countryside. As they drove along, Stanley chattered on and on in his clipped staccato, letting Alban set his own pace.

"Girlie, this is going t' be the greatest honeymoon any beautiful bride could ask f'r! There's s' much t' see and do here, we'll spend all summer at it. We'll have the time of our lives, you bet! Climb Mount McGregor—see Grant Cottage. Go back t' Saratoga and drink all the Saratoga water you want, dance, ride out t' the Lake, and listen t' the band t' your heart's content. Go t' Glens Falls—Aunt Emma and Oscar and Ida Finch live there. See Cooper's Cave. Good place t' shop too, if you want new clothes. Then we'll go t' Lake George. Now there's the spot f'r honey-

64

mooners! You c'n tell your grandchildren some day I took you t' the 'Queen of American Lakes' f'r your honeymoon!"

Hortense was drinking in every word and getting excited at the thought of all those wonderful places.

"You can be my guide everywhere we go, honey, and tell me the story of each place, just like a museum tour guide." she said in her soft southern voice. "Our honeymoon is goin' to be just perfect!"

"All right, young lady," he said with a melodramatic sweep of his arm. "Now cast your eyes t' the right, and you'll see the famous Mount McGregor. Have t' climb it on a cloudless day, so's you c'n see f'r miles and miles.

"Now who do you s'pose the first settlers around here were?" Not waiting for a response, he rambled on. "Mohawk Indians had a trail along the base of the mountain—probably right where this road is. Hunted and fished up the valley here in summer. Found many an arrowhead on the farm when we were cultivating. Hudson River Valley's always been real important t' travelers. Main road from New York t' Montreal, you know. Lotsa days there's fifteen or twenty buggies by our house, going t' Canada! Yessir, it's a real busy road!"

Stanley was taking the tour guide role seriously. He was set to give her a complete history of the area. He went on with his monologue enthusiastically.

"We'll turn here at Van Rensselaer's store, so's we c'n go t' Gurn Spring. Down that way towards Greenfield Center was the Battle of Wilt'n in. . . ."

"Oh, Stanley, I wish you wouldn't talk about Indians and battles," she shuddered. "I don't like to think about them."

"Well, girlie, that's just part of history."

For a moment he was squelched, and they jogged along for a few minutes in silence. Then Stanley had a thought.

"Let's stop at Kilbara's place t'day and see if they have 'ny strawberries t' sell. I do love 'em! Ma makes wonderful strawberry shortcake. And just wait 'til you taste her strawberry preserves!"

"Your mother's a wonderful cook. I've found that out already. I never saw so much food in all my life as she had on the dinner table yesterday. I'm goin' to be fat as a pig, if I keep on eatin' the way I did last night."

Stanley cocked his head on one side and put his hand on his hip.

"Well now, Tiny, I'd say you've got the makings of a right pretty pig!"

Hortense laughed. "You silly, Stanley," she exclaimed and reached over to give him a hug, which ended in a long tender embrace.

Stanley reined Alban to a stop as they reached the cemetery at Gurn Spring.

"Here's where Pa's buried. Died on New Year's Day last year. Let's walk over t' his grave. Ma asked me t' water the geraniums."

Stanley took off his hat and carried the bucket of water to the back corner of the cemetery where several red geraniums were blooming gaily in pots on the grave.

"I wish I'd known your father. Your mother showed me the picture of him on the wagon. He looked like such a dear, kind man. I love that picture of him, sittin' there with all those baskets of grapes. The horses were waitin' so patiently for him to be ready to go to market."

"Yep, yep. Kind man Pa was. Best grapes in Saratoga County. Bought Ray an overcoat one year with money from one wagon-load. Wait 'til you taste 'em!"

"Don't you think we ought to get a copy of that picture, so we could have one to keep?"

Stanley nodded emphatically. "Yessir, I'm sure we could get the photographer in Saratoga t' make a copy of that picture. It's the last one Pa had made. I'll speak t' Ma about it."

They walked back to the buggy and drove off past the church and around to Emerson's store. After chatting a while with the folks gathered at Emerson's, they arranged to pick up a barrel of potatoes on Thursday. Then they stopped at Kilbara's and bought four quarts of luscious, ripe strawberries. As they rode along they couldn't resist sampling a few.

"Better test 'em t' be sure they'll make good shortcake!" Stanley made an elaborate pretense of examining and judging the berries. "Not bad," he said critically.

At Will Pratt's slaughter house, Stanley tried to haggle about the price of the calf Ma wanted to sell, but Pratt was firm in his offer of four cents a pound. Ray had weighed the calf at 347

66

pounds, so Pratt agreed to come and pick it up next week and pay $13.88.

Again they stopped to chat for a few minutes. Everyone was interested in meeting the new bride, and they all found her Southern drawl charming and her sweet smile beguiling. So it went all week. Stanley showed off his bride to all the neighbors. Stanley insisted on doing all the errands, so he would have an excuse to take Hortense all over the community. Their honeymoon seemed more practical than romantic, but each day was packed with pleasure.

"I love Saratoga, Stanley," she exclaimed as they rode. "This fresh air is so invigoratin' it makes me feel marvelous. All the people here are so kind and friendly, and I love you so much! I'm sure I'll love you always—there will never be another man in my life!" She hugged him happily, not mentioning to her husband that his mother still terrified her.

Lottie was more and more aggravated no matter how hard she tried to be patient. Hortense hovered around whenever she was at home, trying so hard to be helpful. The girl was clumsy, ignorant, and inept. She had no idea how to do the simplest household tasks, but kept asking to help and getting under foot, slowing down all the housework. Lottie fumed to herself, If I'd had a daughter she would have known how to do all these things by the time she was twelve years old. How sick I am of all these artificial compliments:

"Mother Bush, you keep the house so neat and homelike. I hope some day I will be as good a housekeeper as you are!"

"That was such a good dinner. Will you teach me some of your recipes?"

"Your handwork is so pretty. Will you teach me how to embroider and how to piece quilts?"

She knew that Hortense and Stanley adored each other right now, but they were so wrong for each other—surely the marriage wouldn't last much more than six months. Stanley's infatuation with this child would soon wear off. It was obviously an unwise marriage too hastily arranged.

Ray seethed in silence. Each day that week he had come in from his work in the barns and fields only to see them driving off

67

in the buggy. They had usurped his duties, taking over all his errands and picking up the mail, so he missed his favorite part of the day—the gossip sessions at the store or at friends' homes.

Hortense was everything he had predicted she would be—a dancing girl, who couldn't cook, sew, or clean. Still he didn't really have anything against her personally, except that in his mind she had become an extension of Stanley. They were inseparable, so he hated them both. He no longer cared about breaking up their marriage—after all she would soon be twenty years old, and that did seem old enough to be married. All he wanted now was for both of them to go away to live in Florida and never come back. He was counting the weeks until time for them to leave. Meanwhile he developed a habit of ignoring them both politely, addressing his remarks to his mother when he had something to say.

# AN IDYLLIC HONEYMOON
## Chapter 7

The newlyweds had been there a whole week before Clif's family arrived to greet them.

"Hi, Uncle Stan!" Harold cried boisterously, recognizing him now. "Boy, am I glad you're back. Is this my Aunt Hortense?"

Hortense leaned down and shook his hand solemnly. "Yes, I'm your Aunt Hortense. Do you know I've never been an aunt before?"

Harold was delighted with this soft-spoken, brown-eyed aunt.

"Ma and me are going t' stay all week. Would you like me t' take you fishing? I'll show you where you c'n hear the echo too."

"I'd love it if your Uncle Stanley can come too."

Everyone laughed. Stanley wagged his finger at Harold and warned him not to try to steal his wife.

"You'll have t' find your own pretty girl, Harold. This one belongs t' me."

Ray took the boxful of baby chicks with the mother hen that Clif had brought to the hen house, while Clif put Delmar in the pasture. Everyone else took parcels in the house. Harold was the last in, because he insisted on being independent and laboriously climbing the steps unaided.

Hortense whispered aside to Stanley, "What's wrong with Harold's legs?" She was terribly upset.

Stanley whispered back, "He had infantile paralysis two years ago."

This was Clif and Mary's first chance to assess the new member of the family, and they liked what they saw. They knew Stanley was like a butterfly that can't be still. Hortense seemed just right for him, except that she was awfully young. Stanley obviously doted on her. He hovered around her constantly.

Hortense's soft laughter was infectious, and her quiet voice caught all attention whenever she spoke. Her manners were dainty and precise, and she was courteous and friendly to everyone. By turns she was childish and serious, gay and pensive, talkative and quiet. Always she was thoughtful, considerate, helpful, and charming. Definitely she was quite the opposite of anything they had imagined her to be before her arrival.

Harold announced in a loud voice between bites at dinner, "Aunt Hortense, I love t' hear you talk!"

She smiled and thanked Harold graciously, as if he had tendered the supreme compliment.

After dinner Hortense drew Stanley aside and asked about Harold again.

"Can't they do anythin' about his crippled legs, honey? I feel so sorry for that cute little boy with such a terrible brace!"

"Ma wrote me they'd gotten the brace last winter. Before that he dragged himself 'round on the ground with his hands. Clif 'n Mary have taken the boy everywhere and consulted with a lotta doctors trying t' do everything possible t' help him."

"I hope the brace helps, or they find somethin' else that will—and soon too!" Hortense exclaimed.

"I do too. That's a real plucky kid. Yessir, crippled legs or no, he's going t' make a fine man some day. Got what it takes. You don't see him sitting 'round complaining 'cause he can't walk like everybody else. Yessir, a fine boy."

On Sunday Oscar and Ida Finch and Aunt Emma came down from Glens Falls. Their reactions to Hortense were similar to everyone else's. Her Southern drawl captivated all of them. Oscar's teasing and old Aunt Emma's critical scrutiny were both received with good humor and gentle friendliness. It seemed impossible for anyone else to resist the demure girl with the beautiful brown eyes, but Lottie and Ray both obstinately withheld their approval.

Mary and Harold stayed all week, and the following Sunday Clif came back in time for dinner. The aroma from the chicken baked pie had just begun to fill the house and arouse appetites. Lottie had killed the big white rooster and cooked it slowly yesterday until it was so tender the meat had almost fallen off the bones. This morning she had added potatoes and just the right amount of salt and pepper and cream to the meat and gravy. Then she added their first fresh peas out of the garden, put her best flaky pastry on top, and there was a meal for the best of company.

Clif was sniffing it hungrily. Mary was upstairs getting hers and Harold's clothes packed, so they could leave right after dinner. Ray and Stanley were out picking a bushel of cherries for Ashley Bush to pick up Monday.

Suddenly an unearthly screaming began—the most horrible noise Hortense had ever heard. She laid down the silverware she had been putting on the table.

"What's that?" she exclaimed in horror.

Mary came running down the stairs.

"Something's happened to Harold!" she screamed.

"Where is he?" asked Lottie, almost dropping the golden brown chicken pie.

The shrill, piercing screech continued and seemed to be somewhere outside.

"That doesn't sound like Harold," Clif said, and he went out the side door to investigate.

The screaming stopped, but a pounding, huffing, and snorting noise replaced the screech. Soon the noise-maker appeared, running full speed toward the barn. It was a large pig who escaped from the pen in the orchard and was looking for protection from his tormentor. Clif caught the frightened animal up against the barn door, just as Ray and Stanley came running to see what had happened.

They noticed that the hair was gone off the pig's back. Some small cuts indicated that the pig had met with some kind of enemy, occasioning his horrible shrieks.

They started leading him back to the orchard, watching along the way for some predator that might have attacked the pig. They walked down past the oat field and were halfway to the Spy orchard when they heard a thumping noise. The men looked at each other, wondering if they should have stopped to get a weapon of some sort.

Presently Harold appeared, clumping along slowly, swinging one braced leg in front of the other carefully, so as not to trip on the uneven ground. In his hand he held a pair of scissors.

Suddenly the men realized what had happened. Harold was the enemy who had attacked the pig!

Clifford dealt with Harold while Ray and Stanley put the pig back in the pen and secured the gate.

"What were you doing to the pig, Harold?" he asked quietly.

"I was shearing him, Pa."

"But we don't shear pigs, Son."

"Well, Uncle Ray sheared the sheep and they look all pink now instead of dirty. I wanted t' see if the pig would look pink too."

"Pigs don't need to be sheared, Harold, but when they're full grown, Grandma and Uncle Ray will sell them for meat. As for the sheep, they must be sheared carefully so the fleece can be sold. Uncle Ray told me he sold 254 pounds of fleece at Saratoga last week for a lot of money—over $48, in fact. You see this is part of Uncle Ray's and Grandma's income that they must have to live on. Now I want you to promise me you'll never try to shear any animal by yourself again."

"Yes, Pa." Harold said hanging his head. "I won't do it again."

Ray and Stanley explained the episode to the frightened women, who were waiting by the oval flower bed for them to come back. Lottie and Hortense exchanged glances. It was all they could do to keep from laughing. Mary was too upset to think it was funny. She would have chided Harold severely if she hadn't been so convinced earlier that he was hurt. As it was, she was relieved that her dear child was safe and no harm was done.

My lands, what mischief would that child get into if he had two good legs? she wondered.

It was not until after every morsel of the delicious dinner had been consumed, and the Clifford Bushes were on their way back to Palmer, that the rest of the family broke into gales of laughter.

"That pig sounded just like a person being murdered!" Hortense exclaimed.

"Harold had such a guilty look—the criminal caught in the act!" chortled Stanley.

"Whatever made him think of such a thing?" asked Lottie.

"He wanted to see if the pig would be pink after it was sheared, like the sheep!" Ray whooped.

"I don't know what he'll think of next!" moaned Lottie.

The band was playing in Congress Spring Park the following Tuesday, and Stanley was murmuring fragments of information into Hortense's ear. She tried to shush him, but he insisted on interrupting the music at intervals all through the concert. They had just swung into Victor Herbert's *Fantasia American*, and Hortense thought it wonderful. She was so thrilled she didn't

72

want to miss a note. But there was Stanley sitting on the park bench beside her, saying, "Victor Herbert used t' conduct the orchestra in the garden at the Grand Union. Here every summer f'r years. They say he was paid great money—bet it all—terrible luck—never had 'ny money t' take home."

When the band launched into its last number, a rousing march by John Phillip Sousa called *The Free Lance*, Stanley had to whisper that Sousa had led the band here in Congress Spring Park for several seasons.

At the end of the concert, the crowd applauded and cheered. Band leader Doring bowed and left the little bandstand set in the middle of the lake. People rose from the park benches and the grass and stopped to chat with friends, rather than hurrying away. There was always a festive atmosphere in the park, but especially at concert time. Stanley introduced his demure little bride to several friends, and a jovial group gathered around them.

"Wasn't that an excitin' concert!" Hortense enthused. She was enthralled by the music, the crowd, and the whole environment.

"Not many celebrities here this year!" commented one of Stanley's friends. Most of the people in the crowd were local villagers or folk from around the county.

"Where d' you s'pose all the elite went this year?"

"I've heard they all went to Europe. With no horse races and no gambling, why should they come to Saratoga?"

"That fool Agnew-Hart Law really hurt business. Ought to be repealed. Saratoga was hit harder than any place else in the state."

Hortense looked from one to the other with a puzzled expression as they discussed it. "Do you mean they aren't goin' to have the horse races in August?" she asked hesitantly. "I thought they always had them."

"No. There were no races last year. Won't be any this year either. No point having races if you can't bet on them. Lotsa people have sold their horses."

"That's right. The hotels are really hurting. They say Congress Hall Hotel's going to have to close down. Shops are empty. Not many tourists come any more just for the spring water. The big spenders are likely in Paris or Rome now."

Hortense had thought it was very crowded, but she couldn't imagine the throngs Saratoga usually had in the summer.

73

They walked along the curving path, stopping to admire the statues and the beds of flowers in full bloom, until they got to the bubbling Congress Spring. Hortense wanted to try the funny, fizzy water again. She giggled.

"It tastes kinda good when you get used to it. But it still tickles."

On the trolley going home, Stanley kept up a constant patter of odd bits of information about Saratoga and the famous people who had frequented the Spa. Hortense listened eagerly. She wanted to hear all of Saratoga's fascinating history.

"Did you ever gamble at Canfield's Casino, dear?"

"Well," Stanley hedged and grinned, "maybe just a little."

He hastened to turn the conversation to someone else.

"Did you ever hear of 'Bet-a-Million Gates'?"

Hortense interrupted as the trolley pulled to a stop in Wilton.

"We'd better get off here, honey. There's Ray with the buggy."

Another exciting day of their honeymoon had come to an end. Hortense loved glamorous Saratoga. She would treasure her visits there for the rest of her life.

"I've had a wonderful day!" she drawled as she climbed into the buggy. "Thank you for picking us up, Ray. You're sweet."

Ray acknowledged her thanks with a noncommittal grunt.

When they got home, Lottie said, "I wrote to your mother this evening, Hortense. I told her you arrived safely and are enjoying your stay here."

"It was nice of you to write to my mother. Yes, I really am enjoying my stay." She thought it would be much nicer if her mother-in-law were not so stern and grim. It would also be nice if Ray could speak to her in sentences instead of unsociable grunts.

The next day Hortense got a thick letter from her father and took it upstairs to read in privacy. When she came down, her eyes were red, as if she'd been crying.

Lottie didn't feel that she could ask her what her father had said. But she knew something was wrong. Hortense was much too reticent about her family and about her life before she moved to Hastings. Why would so young a girl have left home?

The next Sunday afternoon was so clear and bright that Stanley decided it was time to climb Mount McGregor.

"Put on your walking shoes, Tiny. Let's go up on the mountain."

"Oh, goody! I've been wantin' to go!"

This was what she had yearned to do since her first day on the farm. Every day since then, she had gazed up at its mysterious slopes with growing anticipation. In all of its various moods, the mountain beckoned to her with an irresistible magnetism. What delights would its green majesty reveal?

Hortense was accustomed to monotonous flat country with sand dunes as the only hills. Compared to sand dunes, this looked like Mount Olympus.

Bubbling with exuberance, Hortense put her hand in Stanley's, and they started out the back door.

"How do we get there?"

Guiding her by the flower beds and the outbuildings, Stanley said, "Well, we just g' down here past the oat field, through the vineyard and up through the Spy orchard. There's a trail all the way up t' the Cottage and the Lookout. You c'n see the wagon tracks where Ray takes a short cut up the mountain. It's a nice walk—walking's good f'r you. C'mon, there's the Spy orchard just up ahead."

Hortense held back apprehensively.

"Tell me the story about the spy orchard," she said hesitantly.

"What do you mean, girlie? What story?"

"You know. About the spy. Was he caught here in the Revolutionary War?"

Stanley stared at her. Then he burst out laughing.

"You thought there was some horrible story about a spy being caught and killed here, didn't you?"

She nodded, her eyes wide, her chin quivering. Stanley realized once again what an unsophisticated child she still was.

"Bless you, baby, there's no spy. Nobody got killed or even hurt here."

He picked an apple off the tree. It wasn't much bigger than a marble.

"Here's your Spy, sweetie. This hard, little green thing's a Northern Spy apple. Won't be ripe f'r several months. Then it'll be a bright red. One of the finest apples you c'd ask f'r—firm texture, tart flavor. Can't beat it f'r eating raw or cooking 'ny way you want. Now don't you worry your pretty head about spies in these parts. Our only Spies are apples."

"I feel so silly. I was dumb not to know that."

He hugged her. "You weren't dumb at all. Florida Crackers aren't s'posed t' know about apples—just oranges 'n' grapefruit."

They walked on up the mountain, Hortense stopping to look at everything along the way. It was all so different from the flat, hot land she was accustomed to in Florida.

"See the pigs over there under the apple trees, Tiny? Ray puts 'em out here every summer. They root around and keep the orchard cultivated. Now don't worry, they won't bother you."

But Hortense was hurrying to get past the pig pen. Their grunting and snorting seemed ominous to her. She was afraid they would leap over the fence and chase her.

A little farther along the path, Stanley crushed some twigs of hemlock and held them under Hortense's nose. She was delighted with the pungent aroma. Then she saw a strange tree with snow-tipped cones and learned that it was a white pine.

As they walked on, she got more and more excited.

"Oh, my goodness, look at those ferns! They're up to my waist! I've never seen such ferns! How beautiful they are!"

"Ferns like t' grow with their feet in water. Lotta ferns on the mountain, because there's a lotta springs. Our water at the house comes from one like this. Runs all the time, summer and winter, rain or shine."

Hortense picked up two smooth, lovely pebbles beside a small brook, when they started their climb again.

"Why are these rocks so smooth, honey?"

"Hmm. Probably smoothed by the glacier. Formed a lake when it melted. You c'n see different levels of the lake on the side of the mountain."

She looked at him skeptically. She decided he was teasing her, but changed the subject rather than argue with her husband.

"Look, Stanley, don't these look like goose eggs?" She giggled. "They just fit in my hands and feel so comfortable. May I keep them?"

"Well, 'course you can, Tiny. Here's another just about the same size. I'll carry 'em in my pockets. Some day you c'n tell your grandchildren you picked these up on famous Mount McGregor. These are the rare, polished gems found by the beautiful bride on her honeymoon!"

He pranced around, pretending to show the pebbles to an imaginary audience.

"You silly," she giggled and gave him a hug and then a long, loving kiss.

Hand in hand they went on up, walking on a gravel road, when the wagon trail ended, and then on what had been an old railroad bed. Suddenly they came out onto a grassy bank near the top of the mountain. The sun was warm and felt good, after their long tramp under the trees, where it was cool. Puffing from their climb, they sat down to rest on a large sloping rock in the middle of the Eastern Lookout.

Hortense had just breath enough to say, "Spectacular!"

Stanley pointed at a stone marker just to their right.

"That's where President Grant stood t' get his last look out over the valley. Used t' be a pavilion there back in Hotel Balmoral days."

He pointed at the mountains in the distance.

"Those are the Green Mountains in Vermont, clear across on the other side of the Hudson River. Up that way t' the left you c'n see Glens Falls and the Adirondacks. Down the other way is Saratoga. You c'n see Saratoga Lake over there. Look here, Tiny. You c'n see the farm if you stand here and look down. See Ma down there? She just went down the side porch steps, going out t' the oval flower bed. Looks like she's pulling weeds."

"How tiny she looks!"

Hortense's face was a picture of delight. It was the first time she had ever been on a mountain. She gazed down at the farm with its fields all shades of fresh spring green. The cattle were grazing peacefully near the huge red barn. The house glistened white in the sunshine, and in the distance the mountains looked blue and mysterious. The sky was so clear, the breeze so pleasant, and the sun so warm, she wanted the day to last forever.

"Stanley," she said thoughtfully as she sat down on the rock again, "are you sure you don't want us to live here, instead of in Florida?"

He took her hand and patted it.

"Little lady, we can't live here. Summers here are beautiful. We c'n come here on vacations, but you wouldn't believe what the winters are like. So cold and snow so deep—some days it's all you c'n do t' stay alive and keep the animals alive. You don't know how 'tis t' be in twenty-seven degrees below zero weather f'r a week!

77

"No sir, we're going t' live in Hastings until we get rich. Then we'll live anywhere you want."

Hortense laughed. "I don't care about being rich, Stanley. I'll be rich enough if I just have you. If that's where you want to go, it's fine with me. But I wondered if you wouldn't really rather stay here near the farm or in Glen Falls."

"No, baby, farm work's not f'r me. A man c'n spend his life struggling and breaking his back and never have anything t' show f'r it but food f'r his belly.

"As f'r Glens Falls, they have jobs there that could break a man's spirit, though not his back. C'n you imagine me working in a mill manufacturing newsprint, or boxes, or lime? That's dreary work in a dull town. Now that you're my wife, I want t' have a good job where I make a lotta money, so's I c'n make you happy and our children happy some day."

He jumped up. Stanley could never sit still long.

"Come on, baby, I want t' show you Grant's Cottage. It isn't far now. We'll see if the Clarkes are there."

Mrs. Clarke welcomed them at the door and guided them through the Cottage, which was kept open as a shrine. She explained in detail about Grant's last illness and showed them the flowers that had been dried after his funeral.

Finally she suggested that they ask Will Green to show them around the new Sanatorium. Thanking Mrs. Clarke and waving goodbye, they walked up past the site of the old Balmoral Hotel and over to the construction area, with Stanley chattering all the way. He gestured, showing her where the narrow-gauge railway used to run to the hotel, and told her that John Myers used to be a section hand and Clif was a water boy. Then he told her about the fire in '97 and how they could read a newspaper out in the farmyard at the base of the mountain by the light of the burning hotel.

Will Green was happy to show them around, and they marveled at the progress of the stone buildings and imagined how beautiful the whole project would be. The Refectory with its vaulted ceiling over 24 feet high impressed Hortense most.

Stanley took a fancy to the ice house built right into the embankment of an artificial lake on top of the mountain.

"Very nifty," he approved. "Don't even need t' load the ice on a sleigh—just slide it right int' the ice house! What d' you think of that?"

Will went into great detail about the other buildings—the infirmary and the ward buildings a little way down the slope.

"One end of each bedroom will always be open to the fresh air, with a heated dressing room in the rear. There will be a skylight with a ventilator so there's constant circulation of air above the bed. Take a deep breath, Hortense."

Hortense did as she was told.

"People wouldn't ever get sick in the first place, if they always had that nice fresh air to breathe all year round. No stuffy, heated rooms to spread germs."

"I think you're right, Mr. Green. This mountain air makes me feel wonderful. It's so beautiful and so quiet here on the mountain with the rocks and trees and the view. It must be horrible to have tuberculosis, but I can't think of a nicer place to be sick," Hortense drawled.

"Yessir, it's a good healthy climate, all right. It's the altitude does it. Yessir," Stanley jabbered on.

Mr. Green pointed down the side of the mountain to the power house and laundry.

"We'll connect on at the Electric Railroad transformer station, so's we'll have electricity in all the buildings."

"Wouldn't Ma love t' have electricity? Think of being able t' flick a switch, instead of lighting a lamp! Wouldn't that be wonderful? Yessir, that'd be something!"

Stanley would have gone on prattling all afternoon, if Hortense hadn't tugged his arm gently, pointing out that the sun was getting low. She wanted to get down that mountain path before dark. Thanking Will Green profusely for showing them around, she dragged Stanley away, still exclaiming about what a marvelous thing the "sanitarium" was going to be.

When they got back to the spring with all the lush ferns, Hortense asked Stanley to cut some to take home. She held them in front of her like a bride's bouquet. They stuck up four feet in the air, completely obscuring her face.

"How do I look, darling?" she teased.

"Beautiful, as always," Stanley said, pulling the ferns away from her face, so he could kiss her.

It started as a frolicsome joke, but turned into a long, passionate kiss, as their bodies touched and they felt again that exquisite desire. Hortense thought that being married to Stanley was the most wonderful thing in all the world. Surely her love for him would last through all eternity.

Back at home, Lottie put the ferns in a tall urn in the big dining room, while she listened to Hortense's animated account of their walk. Hortense's eyes were full of wonder at everything she had seen. Lottie realized with a start that she could come to care very much for this child, if only she were not her daughter-in-law.

"Today was the most marvelous day of our whole honeymoon. I'll remember it all my life," Hortense said dreamily.

"But, Tiny, you haven't seen Lake George yet! Prettiest place in the whole U.S. of A.! That'll be the best of all!"

Ray stayed busy in another part of the house and didn't listen to Hortense's recital.

"Don't fix supper f'r us t'night, Ma," Stanley said a few days later. "We're going Saratoga early. Get something t' eat there."

"All right, Stanley. You're taking Hortense to the band concert?"

"Yes, indeedy! She loves 'em. Want t' take her t' Yaddo t'day too. Gotta show her all the sights."

They rode to Wilton with Ray when he picked up the mail, and then caught the car to Saratoga Springs.

The "Queen of the Spas" seemed just as glamorous and exciting to Hortense this time as it had the first time she went there almost a month ago.

"D' you realize t'morrow is our anniversary, little lady?" Stanley asked as they stepped off the trolley.

"That's right," Hortense nodded. "Tomorrow we'll have been married one whole month. And I still love you as much as ever!"

"Lordy, Pete, I should hope so! I love you more every day, Tiny."

"I wonder if we'll be able to say that after fifty years, honey."

"I'll love you fifty times as much then, and you'll still be my beautiful bride," he vowed.

Hortense looked pensive. "I'll be seventy years old then," she said, already considering herself twenty.

"And I'll be eighty-four," he answered cheerfully.

Stanley steered Hortense to the High Rock Spring, chattering all the way about the history of Saratoga Springs.

"C'mon, let's have a taste. All the springs taste different."

She made a face over the bubbly water. "It tastes salty—I'm not convinced that it could cure anythin'," she said skeptically.

In a hired buggy they rode to see the enormous Yaddo estate. Stanley told her the tragic story of the Trask family, as they drove through the winding roads past forests and gardens. They glimpsed the lovely Victorian Gothic mansion through the elaborate planting of trees and shrubs. Then they hurried back to town for a quick supper at the Grand Union Hotel before the band concert in the park.

Hortense was subdued and solemn through the concert.

"Why so quiet, sweetie? Don't you like the music?" he asked between numbers.

"I love it—especially the *Pilgrim's Chorus*. That was magnificent. But I keep thinkin' about the Trasks! How terrible to lose all four of their children while they were so young. And the father dyin' in that horrible train wreck.

"I'd like to have four children, honey. Two boys and two girls. Wouldn't that be ideal? We used to have such fun—Eric and Kathleen and me—and you know we had another little brother—Bertram—but he died of scarlet fever when he was only two years old.

"I hope we won't be unlucky like the Trasks, don't you?"

He put his arm around her and gave her a little squeeze. "I'm sure we won't be unlucky, Tiny. You and I have a whole, long, wonderful life ahead of us. Don't you worry."

When the band played selections from the popular operetta, *The Red Mill*, Hortense began to feel better. Her usual good humor returned, and by the end of the concert, she was ready to applaud and then laugh and talk gaily with their friends who were in the audience.

Stanley introduced Hortense to some of the members of the cast of *The Country Doctor*. They had drafted him to help with the coaching and prompting for their play to be presented next week. The young people joked back and forth mysteriously about "Dr. Britton" and "Mrs. Gilbert," but refused to explain anything to Hortense.

"You must come to see the play next Wednesday. We don't want to spoil the surprise for you," Hubert Palmer told her.

"I'm looking forward to it very much. Stanley's told me that you-all are superb actors and actresses. I wouldn't miss the play for anythin'!"

Stanley's friends glanced at each other in amusement at Hortense's southern expression. They liked her soft drawl and her unsophisticated manner.

"Try to guess who the jewel thief is when you see the play, Hortense," one of the girls whispered aside.

Roger Staples called as they left, "Stan, don't forget to ask Dr. Roods if we can borrow his bag for the play."

"Right-o," he agreed.


All four of the Bushes went over on the hill behind the barn on Saturday to pick berries. Hortense and Stanley held hands as they walked through the barn and the pasture, past the buckwheat, undulating in the breeze, and up the hill. Hortense set down her berry pail for a moment so she could take off the bonnet Mother Bush had insisted that she wear. She shook her hair free in the wind.

"That feels better," she said, picking up her pail again and giving Stanley's hand a squeeze. "I've never been so happy in my life!"

She held up her skirt and ran for a minute, until she began to grow short of breath.

"In Florida I wouldn't have dreamed of goin' out to pick anythin' in the middle of a July day in the sun!" she puffed. "But here I am runnin' in the sun, and it feels so good!"

"It's a mite different, isn't it, pet? Muggy and sticky in Florida. Much pleasanter here in summer. Lotta folks here go t' Florida f'r the winter, though. Come back in April or May, when spring comes."

"The air's so fresh here. I love the way it smells."

"That's the timothy hay you smell, baby. Ray and I'll bring a lot of it int' the barn this afternoon."

"What are we goin' to pick this mornin', Stanley?"

"Well, now Tiny, I'm going t' check the raspberries. Ma's picking currants and Ray said he'd cultivate the strawberries."

They reached the raspberry patch, and he handed her several dark red berries.

"Try a sample of the best raspberries in Saratoga County, little lady."

"Mmmm. Delicious! Are there enough ripe ones to fill my pail?" He looked around the end of the row.

"There's lotsa ripe berries here, sweetie, but you'd better not try t' pick 'em. You'll tear your pretty skirt and waist on these prickly old bushes. I'll pick these, and you help Ma with the currants."

"I'd rather stay with you, honey."

He tilted her head up and gave her a long, sensual kiss and said, "I'll miss you, baby, but it's only for an hour or so."

He pointed to where Lottie was already busy picking currants. "You and Ma c'n talk woman talk together."

Hortense was apprehensive about being alone with her mother-in-law, but she went reluctantly to where Lottie was picking the large, sweet White Dutch currants. She commented that in Florida the sun would have been unbearable by this time on a summer day.

"Really?" Lottie queried. "Sometimes I think summer's my favorite season. I love the sunshine and the breeze in summer. When all the fruits and vegetables start coming in, I'm completely happy."

Lottie showed Hortense how to pick the ripest berries, commenting, "These currants and the raspberries will make a lot of jelly and jam."

Hortense made another spunky attempt to win approval.

"Oh, will you teach me to make jelly, Mother Bush? I've always wanted to do that."

"Of course. It's really quite easy. I'll let you help me this time and you can make the next batch by yourself."

Lottie wondered why Hortense's mother hadn't taught her anything. She found it incomprehensible that a girl could get married without knowing anything about how to keep house. She supposed she would have to teach the child to cook.

"You've made a lot of friends around the county, haven't you, Hortense?" Lottie asked, trying to make conversation.

"Yes, everyone has been very friendly, but somehow I feel that one certain person avoids me as much as he can."

"Is that one certain person Ray, Hortense?"

"Yes, it is. Is there some reason why he doesn't want me around?"

"No, I don't think so," Lottie said slowly. "But you may realize by now that he and Stanley have never gotten on well. Perhaps it's Stanley he's avoiding, and you're usually with Stanley."

"Then is there some way that I could get Ray to like me, and maybe he would get on better with Stanley?"

Lottie thought a moment and then said, "If you could ask Ray to teach you some things about the animals that he's so fond of, he might appreciate you more. I've noticed that you're a little afraid of the animals, not being used to them."

Hortense laughed. "That's certainly true, Mother Bush. When I tried to gather eggs the rooster chased me out of the pen, and the pigs grunt and snort so. . . ." Suddenly her eyes twinkled. "I know! I'll ask him to teach me how to milk the cows. Then I can help him, so he doesn't have to do all the milkin'!"

Lottie smiled at the thought of dainty, fastidious Hortense milking a cow. She didn't have too much hope of Hortense being of any real assistance to Ray. She was inclined to do everything so slowly and methodically that it seemed she would never finish. The gesture of good will might be just what Ray needed, though. He really had avoided both Stanley and Hortense as much as possible. It had made their visit peaceful. There had been no unpleasantness, but there had been no sense of comradeship either.

"I'm sure he'll be grateful for your offer to help."

Lottie wondered if she could have been mistaken in thinking something was wrong in Hortense's background. How could anything be wrong with this innocent child?

The following Tuesday, Hortense and Lottie were working together in the kitchen. Lottie was making currant jelly, while Hortense observed each step. Then Hortense made a congealed salad for the Myers. The two women had been discussing the play that Stanley was helping with, looking forward to seeing it the next night. After every rehearsal Stanley had come in chuckling, so they knew it would be funny. After a pause, Lottie changed the subject. She felt now that she could ask Hortense something of a personal nature.

"My dear, I still don't quite understand how you happened to meet Stanley. He said he met you in the general store in Hastings. I believe he told me you were working there. But your parents were living in St. Petersburg. Then your mother and your brother moved to Atlanta. I don't mean to be a nosey old woman, but I

84

can't help being curious. Why did you move to Hastings? And why did your mother leave your father?"

Hortense giggled nervously. "It really isn't as strange as it sounds, Mother Bush. I left home and went to work for my cousin Lilly in the store. I lived at her house. It was perfectly decent. Mother will go back to live with Papa after my sister's baby comes. She's worried about her darlin' Kathleen—doesn't think she can have a baby without her there to help."

"I can certainly understand that. Every mother worries about her children long after they're able to care for themselves. Did I hear a note of jealousy there?"

Hortense hesitated. "Well, maybe not that exactly, but Mother thinks Kathleen is prettier and smarter than I am."

"Why, Hortense, what a thing to say! Anyway, Kathleen must be very beautiful to be prettier than you! Why would your mother think she was smarter than you?"

"Oh, Kathleen was valedictorian of her graduatin' class in high school. I just managed to pass. Oh, I made a few A's, I guess, but I wasn't that good a student."

She was looking morosely down at the calf's foot jelly salad and couldn't meet Lottie's curious gaze. Lottie noticed a tear running down her cheek and realized that she must have hit upon a very sensitive subject. She couldn't resist expounding a little of her homely philosophy.

"Grades don't tell the whole story. I'm sure you have many good qualities that didn't show on your report cards in school. Anyway, mothers should never compare their children. I love my three sons—I can't possibly tell you which one I love the most. They're all as different as they can be." She paused for a moment. "I believe there's something else bothering you. Why does this subject upset you so?"

The tears were flowing freely now.

"Oh, Mother Bush," wailed Hortense. "I'm so ashamed! The reason I left home was because I couldn't face all my friends. You see, I took the examination for a teacher's certificate last fall. I went to Tampa to take the exam, along with a lot of other girls. Then they put an announcement in the paper that everybody passed except one. All my friends were teasin' me—sayin' that I was the one. They thought it was very funny. Then a few days later, I got the letter sayin'. . . ."

85

She broke off and sobbed. Lottie was shocked. Was this the dark secret in the girl's past? No, it couldn't be anything as simple as that. There must be something else. That wouldn't explain the mystery of the problem with her father.

"Oh, you poor dear. You were the one who didn't pass, and you couldn't face your friends. I understand now. They were terribly cruel to tease you like that. They didn't mean to hurt you, I'm sure. Nobody would intend to hurt a lovely, sweet girl like you. There, there."

She patted Hortense's hand and realized that it was the first time she had ever touched the girl.

"It doesn't matter now, Hortense. You're a different person now anyway—and won't be going back where those awful people teased you. Now you're married and have a new life ahead of you. Think of that. When you and Stanley go back to Florida this fall, you'll start keeping house. What does a teaching certificate matter now? Besides, if you really want to earn it, I'm sure you could stand the examination again and pass with no trouble at all."

"Thank you, Mother Bush. You're very kind to say that."

She dabbed at her tears with her handkerchief. Then, recovering some of her composure she said, "I think this salad should stay in the ice box for a while before we take it to the Myers, don't you, Mother Bush? If you don't mind, I think I'll lie down for a little while. The smell of all this food is makin' my stomach feel a little queasy."

"Of course, Hortense. I'll get Ray to take this basket down to the Myers later. They're in a sad way without any help now. You rest until supper time. If you're asleep when Ray and I eat our supper, I'll just save a plate for you to eat with Stanley when he gets in. He'll probably be late getting home from the play practice."

As Hortense started up the stairs, Lottie thought, the smell of food made her stomach feel queasy? They've been married just a month now. My God, she must have already been pregnant when they got married! How could Stanley get involved with such an immoral girl? What more shame could he bring to his poor old mother? They will have to say that the baby is premature if it arrives only six months after the wedding!

Hortense felt better the next evening and responded to the

tension, the humor, and the sentiment of *The Country Doctor* with her whole body. She had never seen a real play before, and she thought it was wonderful.

When it was over, all the players took a bow amidst much applause and enthusiastic cries of "Well Done!" and "Bravo!"

"Here's your bag, Doctor. Thanks for letting us use it," Stanley said.

"Don't mention it. Glad I could help. You folks did a mighty fine job."

"Were you surprised at the ending?"

"Not really. I felt sure it would end happily. Every good doctor should get the lovely bride of his choice."

He gave Mrs. Roods' arm a squeeze and winked at her.

Lottie spoke up with her usual literary style comment. "I felt relieved when Agnes was exonerated. I didn't believe she was a criminal."

Hortense drawled, "I liked Dolly. She was so beautiful and sweet."

"Just like you, Tiny," Stanley said, hugging his little wife. "You could've played the part by just acting natural."

The ticket taker announced the take of $64.90.

"We had 126 adults at 50 cents each and 19 children at 10 cents each. . . ." He did some rapid calculation on a piece of paper. "That covers our expenses—$10 royalty and 15 scripts at 35 cents each—leaving us $49.65 clear profit. All the props for the play were borrowed or donated, so the entire amount will be donated to the Wilt'n Methodist-Episcopal Church."

This news was greeted with applause. The Preacher thanked the players for their wonderful project and said a few words about the joy of fellowship with such good Christian people. Then he called out that it was time for supper.

The play had made a happy excuse for a big community social. Now that the entertainment had gotten everyone in a merry mood, they pulled chairs up to the tables in the balcony or into groups on the main floor of Wilton's Town Hall. They ate their fried chicken, potato salad, baked beans, and cake, amid much banter. Someone had brought a Victrola and cranked it up. Some of the young people began dancing. Toward the end of the evening someone began singing along with the records. Soon everyone was singing *Put Your Arms Around Me, Honey* and *Let Me Call*

*You Sweetheart.* Suddenly Hortense realized that they were all singing especially for her and Stanley. Everyone in the hall was looking at her. She blushed and tittered helplessly. Stanley hugged her and went right on singing.

The only thing that marred the evening was Ray's curt response, when Hortense said, "How debonair you look all dressed up, Ray. It's the first time I've seen you without your work clothes on."

He muttered, "Thanks," but didn't look at her or smile when he said it. It occurred to her too late that she shouldn't have mentioned his work clothes.

Lottie wanted to do some shopping in Glens Falls and decided to take Hortense to visit Ida and Oscar, so on Saturday they caught an early trolley, suggesting that Stanley come up and meet them at Ida's for supper. Lottie's young cousin, Lilian, joined them in their shopping tour when they got to Glens Falls. There were many nice, modern stores and they trooped from Hoffman's to Goodson's and then to Fowler's. Hortense eyed the pretty white lingerie and the hand-embroidered voile waists. She was tempted by fancy chiffons and marquisettes, but then she saw the ladies' bathing suits.

"Oh, Lilian, help me pick out a pretty bathin' suit!" she cried. "Look at this one with the sailor collar. I think I'll try it on."

So amid much giggling and squirming in the small dressing room, she was finally attired in the navy mohair bathing suit with bloomers to match, and with collar and sleeves trimmed in striped galatea.

"Do you think Stanley will mind if I pay $3.50 for this darlin' bathin' suit, Lilian?"

"I think it's a good buy. Here, try on this Kellerman cap with the ear rosettes too. It's satin and just matches your bathing suit. Don't worry," she urged, "it's only forty-nine cents."

Hortense put it on and pretended to dive into the water, even though she really couldn't swim.

"You look just gorgeous! Wait 'til Stanley sees you!"

As Hortense changed clothes again, she defended her expenditure by saying, "I'll really need this bathin' suit, because Stanley said he's goin' to take me to Lake George soon."

Lilian smiled at that. "You'll use it more when you get back to Florida, I suspect," she said gently. "That water in Lake George is positively frigid. Not too many people are brave enough to swim in it."

"Oh," Hortense said, but she bought the suit anyway.

When Stanley got there at 5:00, the shoppers crowded around to show what they had bought. Lottie was very proud of her bargain purchases: a Lawn house dress for $1.00, a Shed-water Foulard for $2.50, a corset for $1.50, a table runner for $2.75, and a tablecloth for $1.50.

"Lordy, Pete!" Stanley exclaimed when he saw Hortense's bathing suit and cap outfit. "Now isn't that something!"

He put his hand on his hip, cocked his head to one side and beamed at his petite wife with approval. He would have thought she was cute in a burlap sack, but she certainly was adorable in the swim outfit.

Ida called everyone to hurry to supper, so they wouldn't be late for the moving picture.

"Are you going with us to the picture show, Hortense? It's starring Billie Burke," Ida asked while they were eating.

"Some friends of mine invited us t' spend the night at their summer cottage at Round Pond," Stanley interrupted. "I want t' show Tiny the Cave, too." He turned to Hortense and asked, "What d' you say we take a tour of Cooper's Cave before we go, Sweetie? After we see the Cave, we'll catch the trolley t' Round Pond. One of my fav'rite places. Bring your new bathing suit along, Tiny. We'll go f'r a swim t'morrow."

He turned to Lottie and said, "Don't look f'r us 'til the last car t'morrow night, Ma. Tell Ray we'd appreciate it if he'd meet us."

They walked the four blocks from Ida's house past the stores and on down to the Hudson River bridge, from which they carefully climbed down the rocky path to the narrow, little cavern.

"This is spooky. I'm frightened," said Hortense, shivering and clinging to Stanley. "I've never been in a cave before."

She let out a sigh of relief when they got back out into the daylight, even though it was only a tiny cave—more of a crevice in the rocks. They climbed back up onto the old iron truss bridge just in time to catch the through car.

It was a happy time for the honeymoon couple. A lot of the past month had been spent in working on the farm, but this was a time to play, to enjoy each other, to be young and carefree. They still had another beautiful month of summer stretching before them. There were still a lot of places Stanley wanted show his bride; a lot of things they wanted to do on this glorious first summer of their life together. Like all newlyweds, they were lighthearted and blissfully certain of a long and contented marriage. They planned to settle down in the fall and start the serious business of working and establishing a home for the lovely little family they were going to have.

"I want to have a baby real soon, don't you Stanley?"

"Sure. Fine with me."

"I think it would be nice to have a little girl first and then a boy."

Stanley cocked his head to one side and said solemnly. "Well, I'm not so sure about that, baby. I think it would be nice to have the boy first."

They both laughed as they got off the trolley at Round Pond.

At the Myers' house one afternoon, Hortense was in the parlor holding the baby, while she chatted with Grace. She talked to him and he cooed; she tickled him and he chuckled; she played peek-a-boo and he chortled. Hugging his chubby little body and poking a finger in his smiley dimples, she decided this was the ultimate joy.

"Grace, you're so lucky! I can hardly wait to have a baby of my own!"

Grace smiled. "Yes, I am lucky, but John and I had been married five years before we had Donald. I think you and Stanley need some time together before you have children to care for."

"I suppose so, but I don't want to wait. My sister Kathleen is expectin' a baby in August, and she's just been married a year. I wonder if she'll have a sweet little boy like Donald."

She rocked the baby with a beatific smile on her face, looking very much like a Madonna. Stanley and John came in from the barn and noticed her rapturous expression.

"Oh, Stanley, I wish I could take Donald home with me!"

"Well, little lady, we'll have a baby of our own one of these days. No need t' steal John 'n' Grace's. Bet Grace 'd pull your hair out if you tried t' take her baby!"

"That's right," John laughed, "but here's something you can take home with you, Hortense."

90

He put a tiny gray kitten down on the floor.

"It's adorable!" Hortense exclaimed, handing the sleeping baby back to his mother.

"He's a nice little Tom-cat, Hortense," John told her. "He'll keep the mice out of the barn. Ray told me he's seen several mice lately."

"Cute little feller—'fraid he might chase the chickens, though," Stanley demurred.

"But they're bigger than he is!" Hortense objected.

The kitten waggled his hindquarters, as Stanley's foot moved. Suddenly he pounced on it so fast that Hortense shrieked with laughter. Scooping him up in her arms, she hugged him as she had hugged the baby, and he began to purr happily.

"I'm goin' to call him Tommy," she said smiling maternally.

When Ray found out about the kitten, he was noncommittal.

"We'll see," was all he said when Hortense told him John had promised the cat would catch all the mice in the barn.

Ever since Hortense's conversation with Lottie in the berry patch, she had put off asking Ray to teach her how to milk the cows. Somehow she was always too busy—going somewhere with Stanley, entertaining company, or helping Lottie with the housework.

Lottie knew that she was afraid of the cows, and she suspected that Hortense was also afraid of her brother-in-law. That wasn't so surprising, because Ray was becoming more and more bitter with each passing day as Hortense and Stanley blithely rode off in the buggy to do the shopping and delivering, while he stayed home doing the heavy, hot field work.

One cloudy, blustery day Stanley went to Saratoga without Hortense. She begged off going with him, because of the sporadic showers that morning.

When the rain stopped, Ray went out in the garden and started picking beans for dinner. Hortense took a deep breath, pulled herself up straight, and went out to help with the beans.

"You have such a beautiful vegetable garden, Ray."

"Thanks." He blushed in confusion, not knowing what to say to his sister-in-law. "Stanley feeling bad with malaria?"

"Yes, he's gone to Saratoga to get some more quinine. He ran out."

"Quinine helps. Only thing that does with malaria."

"I wonder why Stanley gets malaria," Hortense mused aloud.

"He got it in Florida during the Spanish-American War. Lotta the troops did. Had it off and on ever since. Always will."

They picked beans in silence for a few minutes. Finally Hortense found the courage to mention the cows. She spoke softly and hesitantly.

"You have a beautiful herd of cows."

"Thanks."

"You know, Ray, I've been thinkin' that while I'm here on the farm this summer, I ought to learn how to do everythin'—like milk the cows, for instance. Would you teach me how to milk?"

The ridiculous picture of meticulously neat Hortense milking a cow almost made Ray laugh aloud. So as usual with girls, he said the wrong thing.

"Cows about to run dry. Got to take 'em to Varney's to be serviced soon. Have to drop our milk customers."

Hortense felt rebuffed. She didn't know what to say. She pulled a few more beans without comment.

"Is there somethin' else I could do to help you?" she finally stammered, feeling that he would say she could help him by staying out of his way.

Ray stared at the sweet, gentle girl who was trying so hard to be nice to him. Suddenly he realized that he had been holding this innocent, unassuming child responsible for Stanley's taking over his duties. He had been holding a grudge against both of them because they enjoyed the same things he enjoyed—the news and gossip sessions at the store and at friends' homes. Now here was this guileless, soft-spoken young girl, trying to win his favor by helping him with his chores. He wanted to hug her and beg her pardon for the way he had treated her. But Ray didn't know how to talk to a young girl. He couldn't think what to say.

So he simply mumbled, "Thanks for helping with the beans," took the basket, and went into the house.

Hortense started walking dejectedly down the road to meet Stanley, so she wouldn't have to face Ray and his mother in the house.

"So this is an idyllic honeymoon!" she mumbled through her tears.

# A WILD RIDE
## Chapter 8

"I don't like to complain, honey. I've tried not to say anythin' about it, but I haven't felt good for about two weeks. That queasy feelin' keeps comin' back in my stomach. I can't understand it."

Stanley clucked sympathetically. "I'm sorry, sweetie."

"I've never been so happy before in all my life, and we're doin' so many excitin' things. Your mother's meals are marvelous—and I love you so much—but I feel worse all the time."

"I'm going t' have t' put you t' bed early this evening, young lady," he said solicitously.

Stanley had persuaded her to go with him to the orchard to check the Spy crop. It was refreshingly cool under the trees up there on the mountainside. The crop was going to be a good one—all the trees were heavy with apples, no longer like marbles, but about half grown and beginning to blush where the sun hit them. Stanley knocked off a few apples here and there, where they were too crowded.

"Need t' thin these a little more," he said. "Better flavor and quality if they're prop'rly thinned."

Hortense sat down on an old stump to rest. "Why do I have to get a headache and feel so tired, just from that little exercise walking up the hill?"

"I don't understand it either, Tiny. I suppose you're too delicate for this life on a farm. Or maybe you're just tired from all our galavanting around."

"Maybe that's it," she said doubtfully.

"Or it could be you're not used to the altitude after living in Florida."

She nodded. "That's more likely, I think." Then she added thoughtfully, "Your mother must think I'm an awful baby."

Stanley cocked his head. "I wonder if. . . ."

93

"If what, Stanley?"

"Oh, nothing. Just thinking about the apple crop," he fibbed.

The next day Hortense lounged in bed. It was Ray's birthday; he was thirty-seven years old. Hortense had planned to make a cake for him, but she felt too bad.

"I'm baking a chocolate cake for him now," Lottie said, relieved not to have Hortense blundering around in the kitchen.

"I feel so useless, Mother Bush. I wish I could do somethin'. I don't even have a present for him."

"Ray's not accustomed to having much fuss over his birthday, anyway. I bought some nice beefsteaks from Brower, the meat man, for our dinner. That will be celebration enough for Ray."

"Don't cook me any steak, Mother Bush. I don't feel like eatin' anythin' but a little soup."

Two days later Hortense was still in bed and still miserable. Nothing would stay on her stomach. Lottie felt her forehead, but she didn't seem feverish. Something was definitely wrong though. Lottie's suspicion of what was causing Hortense's distress should not have his severe an effect. This was not just a little morning nausea, but a terrible, continuing pain. Finally she suggested that Stanley fetch the doctor, if she wasn't better in the morning.

The next morning was very hot and close. The sun came out after a heavy rain and made everything steamy and humid. Hortense's hair was damp on the pillow. She couldn't get comfortable any way she turned. Stanley wiped her face with a cool washrag one last time before he left.

"Try t' sleep some now, dearest. I'm going t' hitch up the buggy and fetch Dr. Roods. He'll give you some medicine that'll fix you up in no time."

A few minutes later Ray peeked in the doorway to see if she was asleep. He saw her enormous brown eyes looking at him. Her face was thin after four days without being able to eat.

"Come in, Ray," she invited.

He walked in hesitantly.

"Is there anything I can do for you?" he asked.

As he spoke, her question just over a week ago, "Is there somethin' else I could do to help you?" echoed in his mind. He had rebuffed her then. As he looked at her flushed face and saw the suffering in her eyes, he regretted his ineptness and clumsiness.

"Sit down," she said. "You can tell me what you've been doin'."

"Nothing much. Been cutting brush. Weeds grow fast this time-a year. Put the sheep back in the orchard yesterday, so's they'd have shelter from the rain. No shelter in the pasture where they've been."

"You work hard all the time."

"Got to on a farm."

"I admire you for all your hard work and your agricultural knowledge," she said softly with an amiable smile.

Ray blushed. He regretted the irritation he had felt toward her before. On the other hand his malice toward Stanley had increased, because he believed Stanley was responsible for her getting sick. Either she was in a family way (after less than two months) or he had gotten her overtired and run down.

After a pause, he chuckled. "You should see the two ladies downstairs. Stopped their auto here, 'cause one of 'em spilled chocolate all down her skirt. Wanted to wash the spots off before they dried. Ma's helping her. You never know who'll knock on your door next."

"Your Ma's nice to everyone, no matter what they need."

Ray looked down at his big hands. He had been twisting his fingers and cracking his knuckles nervously.

"Ma's nice, all right," he mumbled, thinking, but I'm not. No pretty girl'd ever say that about me.

Dr. Roods came in prattling cheerfully about the warm weather. He prodded Hortense here and there, took her temperature, gave her some little pills to take, and pronounced that she should be better in a day or two.

"Just a little liver complaint. Happens a lot in hot weather. Call for me again if she's not better by Wednesday, Stan."

While the men worked outside, Lottie sat with Hortense and worked on her embroidery, chatting to keep up the sick girl's spirits. She had never been this sick with any of her pregnancies, but she had heard of women having to stay in bed the whole nine months. She was sure that must be the problem, aggravated by a little summer flu. No matter how much Lottie wanted grandchildren, she didn't feel that this girl was the proper mother for them.

That afternoon when Will Pratt came by for the old hog, he clucked sympathetically as he made out a check for $19.20.

"I'm mighty sorry to hear that Hortense is sick. She's such a pretty little thing. Why, she oughta be worth at least a dollar a pound!"

He drove off laughing heartily at his joke. Ray stared after him, thinking it a very tasteless joke for a butcher to make.

As soon as Ransom Varney finished his reaping, he brought back Ray's reaper, which he had borrowed. All the neighbors nearby shared tools and equipment, which made good sense, so each farmer wouldn't have to buy all the tools needed on a farm.

Stanley was hitching Billy and Alban to the reaper, when he saw Aunt Lydia come puffing up to the house, her hat flopping in the breeze.

"Aunt Lydia, you shouldn't have walked all the way up here on a hot day like this!"

"When you're eighty-two years old, you'll know you don't like anybody telling you what to do, young fellow," she retorted. "How's that lovely wife of yours?"

"Not good. I'm real worried about her, Aunt Lydia. Doc Roods gave her some pills. Didn't seem t' help a bit. Can't keep anything on her stomach. Ma's given her barley water, soup, ice cream. Nothing helps."

"I'll go in and sit with her a bit. Maybe get her mind off her stomach."

"Fine, fine. Wish I could stay with her too. Got t' cut the oats while the fine weather holds. Got three loads int' the barn already. Havta use the reaper before somebody else needs t' borrow it. Hope this sunshine holds out two-three days so's the oats c'n dry, and we c'n get 'em all in."

Aunt Lydia missed the last part of his explanation. She had started on in the house, knowing he would go on talking as long as she stood there.

Hortense smiled rather weakly at Aunt Lydia.

"I'm glad you came," she said.

"Lottie's a good nurse, but maybe you'd like somebody else to talk to for a change," Aunt Lydia said cheerfully.

Lottie worked on some pillowcases, while they chatted in Hortense's airy bedroom. She was embroidering a B on them, as a wedding gift to Stanley and Hortense. She had already given them two chamber towels with a matching monogram.

Aunt Lydia glanced out the window. "I see Ray leading one of your cows down the road," she mentioned casually.

"Yes, he's taking her to Ransom Varney's."

"I'm sure Ransom's bull will enjoy her visit," the old lady quipped.

"He brought the last cow right back—didn't even have to leave her overnight. We need to have two other cows bred soon too, so they'll calve in the spring."

"That's right. Keep those Guernseys producing that delicious milk, cream, and butter."

"They earn quite a good sum of money for us each year that way. Then there's the money from the veal calves too. And of course the pigs grow fat on the skim milk."

"I like the pot cheese too," Hortense spoke up. Then she added wistfully, "I never did learn to milk a cow."

The older women laughed at that. They assured her they had both milked enough cows to count for her too. Lottie thought her young daughter-in-law sounded sad, as if she would never have another opportunity to learn. Did she think she was going to die?

"The men will be in for supper soon. I believe I'll go start the fire. Aunt Lydia, you entertain Hortense while I get supper."

Lottie put down her embroidery and went downstairs.

Aunt Lydia commented, "You know, this is the loveliest room in the house. It's bright and has such a nice view of the trees and fields."

The lace curtain fluttered gently in the breeze.

"And you get a grand breeze up here. You picked a good place to be sick, my dear."

Hortense was startled by that remark. She thought for a long moment with a frown creasing her forehead. Her voice quavered as she asked finally, "Aunt Lydia, do you suppose it's possible that I have tuberculosis?"

"Certainly not, Hortense. You'd be coughing if you had that. I think you just have an aggravated case of summer complaint."

Hortense sighed with relief. "I hope you're right. I can't think of anything worse than tuberculosis."

While the stove was heating, Lottie picked a lot of lettuce and other salad greens. The garden was producing much more than they could use. She gave Aunt Lydia some garden sauce when she went home that night.

Two days later Hortense was still in bed, was feeling somewhat better, when she learned that it was Lottie's birthday. She was sixty-six years old.

"Oh, Mother Bush," wailed Hortense. "I ought to get up and make you a birthday cake. You must think I'm a terrible hypochondriac. Here I've been in bed a whole week, and you've been runnin' up and down all those steps takin' care of me. Now I don't even have a birthday present for you!"

"Now, Hortense, please don't fret about that. I don't need a thing for my birthday. I only wish I could make you well."

"I feel a little better today. Perhaps I can eat some of your delicious soup today."

Hortense looked thoughtful for a moment. Then she brightened considerably.

"I know what I want to get you for your birthday. I just thought of it. You'll love it!"

"What is it?"

"Oh, I can't tell you now. It must be a surprise. Maybe I can find it when we go to Saratoga or Glens Falls next time. It's somethin' I've wanted you to have since the first day I came here."

"I can't imagine what it is, but I'm sure I'll like it very much."

"I think you will. I promise I'll get it for you as soon as I can."

"Don't worry about that. I'll enjoy anticipating it and wondering what it could be."

In spite of her determination not to get attached to her, Lottie had become very fond of Hortense during the past week. She put down her handwork and fluffed Hortense's pillows.

"Do you think the new medicine Dr. Roods left you yesterday is helping?"

"Yes, I think so this time."

"I hope so." Lottie stood looking out the window. "It looks like rain today. The oats will be ruined if they get wet now."

The clouds looked quite dark and threatening. It was always a race between the men and horses with the horse-rake and the summer thunder storm.

"I see Minnie Varney coming up to the house, bringing you a bowl of something. George is with her. Do you feel like seeing them?"

"Yes, of course. Everyone has been so kind to me. You have wonderful neighbors!"

Later in the evening, when the Durkees and Walter Fullerton

came to call, she felt worse again. Everyone saw how tired she was, and they didn't stay long.

On their way out, they stopped to chat with Lottie and Ray downstairs. Ray opened his mouth to try saying something charming to Ethel Durkee, who was a very attractive young lady, but suddenly he noticed that she was holding hands with Walter. Why were all the pretty girls already spoken for? he wondered. He slumped away dejectedly.

As they left, Elmer and Luella Durkee made Lottie promise to notify them immediately, if they could help in any way.

"You could have the Varneys phone us and we could be here inside of an hour. If Dr. Roods decides to put her in the hospital, we'll come straight here and take her in our auto. She doesn't look at all well," Luella said.

"Thank you, Lu. I'll let you know if we have to put her in the hospital. I believe she's just weak now from lack of nourishment. Perhaps tomorrow she'll be all right."

"Keep us informed, Lottie," Elmer insisted.

"I will, thank you."

Since Hortense had gotten sick, Stanley had hovered nearby, and it was Ray who had to do the errands. The pleasure had gone out of them though. Everyone he met inquired anxiously after Hortense. They had all grown to love her. Ray had to report one day that she was better, another day that she was worse again. Dr. Roods' pills seemed to help for a while, but still no solid food would stay down.

A few days later Ray came home from Wilton with a present for the sick girl.

"I brought you this, Hortense." He held out a bottle of the famous Saratoga Spring Water. "Ryan had some down t' the Bar next to his Livery Stable. I thought it might taste good for a change after barley water."

"Thank you, Ray. Yes, that would taste good. I'll have some on a little ice for my supper. Your Ma is making gruel for me. Maybe now I'll get well.

"Everyone has been so nice—coming to visit, sending cards and letters, bringing food and candy—Mame King brought me some peppermints yesterday. Your mother has pampered me outrageously, and that ice cream you and Stanley made was delicious! If only I could eat more than a spoonful before I vomit again."

99

She smiled weakly. Talking that much had drained all her strength. Ray thought she looked weak enough to die. Almost two weeks she had been lying here, hardly able to eat a thing. Ray's guilt about the resentment he had felt earlier was tormenting him. It was almost as if he had caused her illness, because of his unreasonable and stupid rejection of her. What if she dies? he thought, and immediately thrust the thought out of his mind, lest it show on his face.

"Sit down, Ray, you must be very tired," she said.

I'm not worthy to sit down in her presence, he thought wildly, but he pulled a chair near the bed and sat down. He began talking about the people he had seen and things he had heard in the village.

"The pageant begins tonight in Saratoga," he said, grasping for some more interesting topics for conversation. "It'll go on all week. From what everybody says, it'll be spectacular. Lots of people I know are gonna be in it. Maybe you'll be well in time to go see it."

He knew she wouldn't. Maybe she would never be well. If she died he would blame himself. He had wished her away, but not dead. Oh, why had he hated her? She had never done anything to deserve his hatred. What if Stanley had never married her? He would still resent Stanley, but not this sweet, innocent girl. He realized how unjust and unkind his feelings had been. He had been careful not to voice his anger, remembering his promise to Ma. Still, he knew that she had sensed his resentment and been hurt by it.

It was all Stanley's fault though. He needn't blame himself. Maybe Stanley had gotten her pregnant. Definitely he tired her out with those trips to Saratoga and Round Pond and all. He cursed Stanley for causing this dear, lovely girl's illness.

Earlier he had hoped to break up their marriage in some way, but certainly not by Hortense's death. That possibility never occurred to him. Now suddenly it appeared that death might be imminent. For the first time Ray realized that he had become devoted to Hortense—in fact he loved her dearly. She deserved to live—of course she deserved a better life than Stanley could give her—but at any rate, he didn't want her to die!

What could he say to her when he felt that each day might be her last day on earth? Ray was confused and upset. He cracked

100

his knuckles and wiped sweat from his hands on his pants. His mind sent up an anguished prayer. Please, God, don't let her die!

"Maybe we could all go to the pageant together next weekend," he said aloud.

"I'd like that," she said softly, "but I'm so tired. You go and tell me about it when you get back. I'll enjoy hearing all about it."

He nodded dumbly.

On Saturday nobody felt like going to the Pageant. Ray paced back and forth for a while, not wanting to have a good time when Hortense was so ill. Feeling that he was in the way and that nobody needed him, he finally went by himself.

Hortense was delirious most of the day. She tossed about on the bed without seeming to recognize anyone. She called for her mother. She begged Kathleen to bring her a drink of water.

"What's wrong with Bertram?" she asked once. Her younger brother, Bertram, had died of scarlet fever many years ago.

She held Stanley's hand tightly and said pleadingly, "I don't want to die!"

He soothed her, patted her hand, mopped her forehead with a damp rag, and tried to calm her.

Dr. Roods came in excited about the two hundred people that had just arrived on three chartered trolley cars from Glens Falls.

"They brought the Glens Falls band with them. They're going to have a basket picnic on the mountain," he told Lottie.

"Well, I declare!"

Then in a confidential tone she informed the doctor that she suspected Hortense might be in a family way.

"I don't think so, Lottie," was all he would say. Then he went upstairs and checked Hortense's temperature. "Barely a hundred degrees." He was frankly puzzled. "It's odd that she should be so ill without a higher temperature. If it goes any higher I'll suspect appendicitis." He closed his bag. "Let's watch her closely now. I'll be back first thing in the morning."

He started toward the door, then turned back and reached in his pocket.

"I almost forgot, Stan. I was in the Post Office and mentioned that I was coming to see Hortense. Leslie Van Rensselaer gave me this letter to bring to her. It's from Atlanta. Maybe it'll cheer her up."

Stanley opened it and read it to her, but in her delirium he doubted that she realized what it said. He would have to tell her the big news again later, when she was more herself.

August 21, 1912

*Dear Hortense,*

*Congratulations! You are the Aunt of a fine bouncing baby boy, Richard Clinton Dale, born Tuesday August 20, 1912 at Dr. Noble's Infirmary, weighing in at 8 pounds even. Mother and baby are doing fine. Mother Estes is in full charge here. Hope you are over your indisposition and will soon arrive to pay homage to your new nephew.*

*Regards to 'Uncle Stanley.'*

*Hastily,*
*Russel*

Stanley finished reading the letter and repeated its news to her several times.

"Kathleen's had her baby, Tiny! What d' you think of that? It's a boy. Isn't that wonderful?"

"Kathleen says Bertram is dead," she muttered and tossed her head, her hair sticking to her damp forehead.

Stanley paced the floor several times, then turned back and observed her tortured face and emaciated body. Emotion that had been building up for days now completely overwhelmed him. He sat on the edge of the bed and buried his face in her hair. He kissed her fevered face over and over again. He clasped her hands and held them tight.

"Oh, God, please don't take her away from me," he whispered. "Our Father, who art in Heaven—Oh, God, I can't remember! What is that psalm? The one about 'the valley of the shadow of death'? God, please don't let her die. We've only been married two months! Please, God, not now—we've only begun to live!"

Hortense had tried to persuade him to go to church, but he had found an excuse every week. "Why didn't I go? Oh, God, I'll go to church—I promise—if you'll just let her live!"

Clif and Mary heard him muttering his prayers as they tiptoed in and spoke to him.

"She's real bad off," he said in response to their questions. "Doc says she might be getting appendicitis."

102

Harold clumped in as quietly as he could. He walked over to the bed and stood looking down at Hortense.

"How're you feeling, Aunt Hortense?" he asked solicitously. He adored his pretty aunt and was hurt to see her look so ill.

"Eric, is that you? I thought you were dead too," she said, and went back to tossing her head on the pillow.

Tears rolled down Harold's cheeks. He turned to his mother.

"She doesn't reckanize me," he wailed.

"She's delirious, darling. That means she doesn't know what she's saying. Come with me and let's see if we can help Grandma with her ripe cucumber pickles."

"All right, Ma."

"Stan, I'll bring Hortense some broth in a few minutes. Your Ma is overrun with all those cucumbers. I'll get our supper a little later."

Harold limped slowly out of the room and down the hall to the back stairway, holding tightly to Mary's hand. His face was streaked with tears. Mary couldn't offer him much comfort. She too had been overcome with emotion. She was very much afraid that Hortense wouldn't live until morning.

Ray came in from the pageant and remembered his promise to tell Hortense all about it. He was bursting to talk about the long and colorful enactment of the history of Saratoga, from the first settlers, who came from Holland, to the glamorous 19th century life in Saratoga Springs. The words Katrina Trask had written to the tune of America were ringing in his ears, "All folk upon the earth sprang from one common birth. . . ."

He went up to Hortense's bedroom. Stanley was sponging her face trying to get the fever down.

"Bury me next to Bertram, Papa," she was saying when Ray walked in.

The two brothers carried on a conversation in whispers.

"She's delirious, isn't she?"

Stanley nodded. "Been this way all day."

Ray felt like knocking his brother flat. He was convinced more than ever that it was all Stanley's fault.

"Doc says she's threatened with appendicitis. He's coming back in the morning. Might have t' put her in the hospital."

Downstairs, Lottie was adding her salty tears to the brine for the pickles. Her guilt over her rejection of that poor child was

103

overwhelming. If Hortense should die Lottie's conscience would never let her rest. She visualized Hortense lying still, fever raging, unable to move her legs—just the way Harold had lain upstairs here in his little bedroom. It was just over two years ago that he was so frighteningly ill, and nobody knew what was wrong with him. What if Hortense had polio too? Was she going to be paralyzed and never walk again without crutches or a brace? Or would she be confined to bed for the rest of her life like Frances? Jennie Varney had died after being sick less time than Hortense. Was Hortense going to die? Would her new daughter not ever reach her twentieth birthday?

When Mary, Clif, and Harold had come in, Lottie was too overwrought to talk to them. It was not Lottie's way to voice her fears; she kept them bottled up inside, but the tension showed in her face and the hunch of her shoulders. She was not even aware of the tears trickling down her wrinkled cheeks, but Clif and Mary understood the gravity of the situation as soon as they walked in. They hugged her and went to check on the sick girl.

Lottie felt wretched and helpless, because she wasn't doing anything for Hortense. Here she was cutting cucumbers and making pickles, when she wanted to be sitting with the sick girl and ministering to her needs. Stanley had shooed her out, though, and Dr. Roods had assured her that everything possible was being done for Hortense. Now Mary was here, trotting back and forth from the kitchen to the sick room, urging Lottie not to waste her crops and insisting that Hortense was being expertly cared for.

The next day was Sunday, and Dr. Roods came twice to check on Hortense. He shook his head.

"I just can't understand it. I've never seen a case of appendicitis with such a low temperature. But I don't know what else it can be. Give her a teaspoon of this syrup every hour that she's awake. Someone must stay up with her all night tonight. I'll come back early in the morning."

Monday morning her temperature had risen to 100.4 degrees.

"I think we'd better take her to Saratoga Hospital," Dr. Roods said finally.

"I'll call Durkees," Ray said and rushed out. He strode down to Varney's as fast as he could go and phoned Elmer Durkee.

"Can you come right away? Doc Roods says Hortense has appendicitis and must go t' the hospital immediately!"

"We'll be there in forty-five minutes," Elmer shouted and hung up.

Ray insisted on carrying Hortense to the touring car, when Elmer and Luella arrived. Stanley got in the back seat and held her head in his lap. Elmer drove off in such haste that Lottie feared he might wreck the auto on the way to Saratoga.

As they went through Wilton a few raindrops began to fall. A loud clap of thunder made Hortense jump and scream.

"I've been shot!"

She held her stomach.

A sudden downpour began drenching them. Elmer pulled into Will Green's barn, which was close to the road and put up the top of the car.

"That'll help some," he said. "Maybe we'd best wait here until the worst of the storm is over."

"I'm afraid to delay getting her to the hospital," Luella exclaimed anxiously.

Stanley was bending over Hortense, stroking her hair and face. He talked to her soothingly. Her eyes were bright with fever and fright.

Luella wrung her hands.

"Why did this storm have to come right now?" she moaned.

"Surely it won't last but a few minutes. Golly what a cloudburst!"

"I've never seen such a hard rain before!"

Suddenly the world seemed to explode. A terrific crash came simultaneously with a brilliant flash of light.

Hortense reared up from Stanley's lap and screamed, "Fire!"

Stanley held her close and tried to reassure her.

"It's only lightening, pet," he said. "There, there, don't worry."

A horse was whinnying in alarm. Rain was pounding on the roof. A door banged in the wind. The horse reared and kicked the wall of his stall. There was a loud roaring noise.

Hortense screamed again, "Fire!"

Her eyes were wide with terror.

Another door banged and Will Green was standing in the barn staring at the automobile. He held a sack in his hand.

"Get out!" he yelled, as he threw the sack over the horse's head and began leading him out. "Get out! The barn's on fire!"

105

Elmer cranked the engine, thankful that it started right away. Jumping back in the car quickly, he backed out into the downpour.

They all looked at the high flames in amazement.

"The barn's going to burn down!" exclaimed Luella. "Look, the whole roof is blazing already. All this rain can't even put it out."

"Too bad." Stanley said. "Will's already brought in all his hay and oats too. He'll lose the whole year's crop. It's going up like a torch!"

"We'll have to go on to Saratoga in the rain," Elmer decided. "We're wet anyway. We've got to get Hortense on down there. I wish we could help Will somehow, but there's nothing we can do here."

He could hardly see ten feet ahead, as he steered along the narrow, curving road.

"Can't you go any faster?" Luella asked nervously.

"I'm afraid I'll run off the road, if I do!"

Hortense seemed to have lapsed into a coma. Stanley kissed and hugged her, but her eyes were closed now, and there was no response, as they continued on their wild ride. She was still breathing,so he knew she was alive, but he was terribly perturbed.

"Spread this rubber coat over her, Stanley," Luella instructed. "The rain's blowing in on her."

"I don't believe Will can save 'ny of his equipment out of the barn," Stanley said, as he tucked the coat around Hortense.

"Good thing he only had one horse in there. If it had been winter, the barn would have been full of cows, pigs, and chickens. He might have lost the lot of 'em," reflected Elmer.

As they pulled into Saratoga Springs, the rain stopped almost as suddenly as it had begun. At the hospital, Hortense was taken directly in for immediate surgery.

Stanley hovered near the operating room. He walked back and forth; he sat down; he got up; he asked the nurses for information every five minutes. They understood his torture—the agony of not knowing whether his darling wife would live or die.

"The doctors are doing all they can for her," they tried to comfort him.

When he was back a few minutes later, a sympathetic nurse said, "No, sir. If she had died on the operating table, they would have told you."

At noon a friendly nurse brought him a lunch tray. He stared at it blankly and never touched it.

Hortense was in surgery most of the day. Toward evening a doctor told him she was out of surgery. She was alive. He didn't promise that she would live until tomorrow.

"You may see her for five minutes. Then I want you to go home and rest. We'll take good care of her. Tomorrow when she wakes, she'll want to see you. Come back then, but for now you need to sleep, or you'll be in here as a patient yourself."

The doctor had seen the fatigue on Stanley's face. Stanley had sat up with her every night, grabbing quick cat naps when she slept, and waking when she called for water or a cool washrag.

"Okay, Doc. I'll try t' sleep tonight."

So he peeked at Hortense, who was snoring heavily, the odor of ether on her breath. She was alive. The look of pain was less intense on her face, but maybe it was just that the anesthetic had numbed the pain.

He caught the trolley and went home.

Tuesday morning Stanley was back at Saratoga on the first trolley. He took comfort in every breath Hortense drew all day, and agonized with every moan. "Not out of danger yet," the doctor had said. That meant the doctor wasn't sure she would live either. Stanley continued his vigil until the nurses shooed him home again for the night.

It wasn't until Wednesday night that he could at last report to his family that she was comfortable. The doctor had finally said that he believed she was out of danger.

"Uncle Stanley," Harold said, standing next to his chair, "if Aunt Hortense is better, why didn't you bringed her home with you?"

"She'll have t' stay in the hospital a long time, Harold. Doc said at least a week more. She's been a very sick little lady."

"I'm sorry she's sick. I made this f'r her t'day. Will you take it t' her t'morrow?"

Harold thrust a piece of paper into Stanley's hand. It was a picture of a round green bowl filled with yellow and orange flowers.

"Those are nasty-turshums," he said proudly.

"Um-hum. Very pretty, Harold. I'm sure your Aunt Hortense

will like that picture. Yessir, that ought t' make her feel better right away."

Stanley patted Harold on the back. He had a great deal of affection for his spunky little nephew. He watched Harold's clumsy steps toward the dining room.

"That boy may have trouble walking, but he'll never have 'ny trouble twisting people's hearts 'round his little finger," he said softly to Mary. "You got a mighty fine boy there."

Ray walked home from Wilton after the last trolley. He came in talking animatedly about the Ballston Fair. Going to the fair was one of the most exciting events in Ray's life—his only chance to get away from home for a whole day.

Lottie had told him she would do his chores, so he could enjoy a day off. This time Mary helped too. Harold insisted on trying to milk the only cow still in milk. He was very awkward, with his brace getting in the way, and he spilled more milk than he got into the bucket, but he enjoyed helping.

"I saw your Pa at the fair, Harold," Ray told him. "Your Uncle Rheinhold was there too."

"You should of taked me t' the fair, Uncle Ray. I wanted t' go too."

"You would have gotten too tired, Harold," Mary reminded him.

"I wish you could've seen the little dog named Dixie, Harold. Dixie is the world champion somersault dog. You would've loved to see that dog tumble!"

"Wow! A dog that can really turn somersaults—head over toes?"

"That's right, and do lots of other tricks too."

Ray turned to his brother and asked anxiously, "How's Hortense, Stan?"

"She's quite comfortable today. Doc says she's going t' be all right."

"Isn't that wonderful!" Lottie said smiling happily.

Ray's face brightened like a sunny day.

"What a relief!"

"Nurse Evans says she's a model patient."

Even on her worst days Hortense had charmed all the nurses with her smiling appreciation for all their attention and her patient endurance of pain. Everyone on the floor had fallen in love with the sweet, young bride, and each nurse had tried to give her extra special care.

Ray realized for the first time that night that his dream wife had taken on Hortense's features. Her large brown eyes gazed at him with just the same admiration, and her smile had the same sweet expression.

"You have such a beautiful vegetable garden," she had said, just as 'Eve' always complimented him.

He was glad Hortense was on the road to recovery—but Stanley didn't deserve her. If only Ray could have a wife just like Hortense, wouldn't that be heavenly!

# RECUPERATION
## Chapter 9

For several days Hortense seemed to be improving, but one evening Stanley came home and sat down with his head in his hands, his elbows resting on the table. He looked completely dejected. Lottie put a comforting hand on his shoulder.

"Was Hortense feeling worse today?" she asked gently.

"No, no. She's better, Ma. Doc says she's out of danger. Going t' be okay. He said it was a near thing though."

Lottie knew something was bothering him—she waited for him to say what it was. Finally he blurted it all out in one anguished breath.

"I was s'posed t' report f'r work next Tuesday morning in Hastings, Ma. Doc isn't going t' let Tiny out of the hospital f'r another week. Says she can't travel f'r at least a month after that. What am I going t' do, Ma? I can't leave Tiny here and go to Hastings. They won't hold the job f'r me. I'm writing to J. B. Nix resigning my job. Got t' find another job after she's well."

"How about the company you worked for in Glens Falls, dear?"

"No!" he exploded. "I'm going t' take Tiny back t' the south before cold weather sets in. She's too delicate f'r these New York winters."

"Those Florida summers are awfully hot though, aren't they? She talked a lot about how pleasant the summer was here. I didn't think she really wanted to go back to Florida."

She sat down across the table from Stanley and started searching for a solution to the problem. Soon she had a suggestion for him.

"Why don't you write to her brother-in-law in Atlanta? Maybe he could help you find a job there."

"I don't think he'd help me, Ma. Don't think Russel has much use f'r me."

110

He paused thoughtfully.

"Atlanta might be a good idea, though. Tiny'd like being near her sister—especially with the baby and all. Winters aren't too bad there, I've heard. Think I'll write t' her Cousin Annie Lawrence. Maybe she c'n help me."

So he scratched off a quick letter and got it ready to mail next morning in Saratoga.

"Here comes Pa!" shouted Harold, and he hobbled stiffly as fast as he could to meet him on the porch.

Clif swung the little boy up and gave him a big bear hug.

"Look what I've got here, Son—peaches, pears, some of the new grapes from California . . ."

"Oh, boy, candy!" Harold exclaimed. "I'll carry that."

He carried the Lifesavers in carefully for his Grandma.

"You should see where Will Green's barn burned, Pa. Uncle Ray drove us down there. Ugh, it looks awful bad!"

"I'll bet it does. Too bad it burned! Have you been a good boy this week, Harold?"

"Course I have, Pa. Aunt Hortense went t' the hospital, but she's better now."

"Yes, your Ma wrote me about that. I'm sure glad she's better, aren't you?"

"I'm sure glad too," Harold mimicked.

Stanley had cheered up, now that he had a possible solution to his dilemma. His darling bride was going to recover. That was all that really mattered anyway. He would take any kind of job for the time being, whenever she was able to travel. They would manage somehow.

Everyone was cheerful around the supper table. They had been under so much tension lately that it was a big relief to laugh and talk like old times.

"Guess where I'm going next Tuesday, Uncle Stanley," piped Harold, his face beaming.

Every time he thought about it, he got so excited he couldn't sit still.

"Let me think," Stanley said solemnly. "Must be somewhere important. Could it be the store? No, no, that's not it. Don't tell me." He paused. "I'll bet you're going to a moving picture show. Is that right, Harold?"

"No," Harold shouted. "I'm going to *school!*"

111

"By golly, that's right. How could I forget that?" Stanley exclaimed and chortled at the joke on himself. "You're six years old now, and you're going t' school!"

"I'm going t' learn reading, and writing, and rhythm-tick, and all like that," Harold said proudly.

"You learn all you can, my boy. That's what's important. Get all the education you can, and when you grow up you'll be *somebody!*"

Harold strutted away from the table looking important and self-satisfied.

"Can you stay over until Monday, Clifford?" Lottie asked.

"No, Ma, we're going to keep the store open on Labor Day. Can't afford to lose all the business we'll get that day. We'll leave right after dinner tomorrow."

"And the next time we come back t' see you, I'll know how t' read and write, Gramma!" promised Harold seriously.

Lottie was too busy to rest on Labor Day either. The canning and preserving had to be done fast when the vegetables and fruits ripened. She sliced a peck of green tomatoes and put them in brine for their favorite green tomato pickle. Then she canned ten jars of plums for winter desserts.

When the jars were cold, Lottie carried them to the cellar and hung the lantern on its hook. Then she arranged the plums on the shelf beside the peaches, pears, and preserves.

Looking around proudly, she thought with satisfaction that her cellar really looked like an exhibit room at the county fair. The shelves were filling up rapidly with a plentiful supply of fruits and vegetables to last until next summer. She felt very prosperous and knew they would certainly not go hungry this winter.

While Lottie was in the cellar, Tommy had killed another chicken. Ray was furious. Then the kitten had the audacity to turn around and cock his head on one side, leering up at Ray and meowing for his dinner—all the while a chicken feather was hanging out of his mouth. Ray grabbed the axe and chopped off Tommy's head.

Instantly he felt anguish and remorse. He loved animals—how could he have done that? Since the cat was destroying his food supply, there was a clear justification for his action, but how Ray wished he had not been the agent of his death. He thought of all the animals he had cared for over the years. Besides all the farm

112

animals, he had nursed an injured fawn, a bird with a broken wing, and a baby rabbit when he was a boy, always feeling a deep sympathy with every living creature.

Several days ago he had taken Tommy surreptitiously back to John Myers' barn. John would just think Tommy had wandered back on his own accord; so would everyone else. After stalking the chickens for three weeks and killing two of them, the rapidly growing cat had worn Ray's patience too thin. His strategy didn't work though—the kitten was back in Ray's barn the next day.

"Poor Tommy," Ray said sorrowfully, as he buried the cat, "you should've stayed in the Myers' barn.

"Hortense! My God! Hortense will be furious if she ever finds out what I did. I'll have to tell Ma, but maybe I can persuade her not to tell Hortense."

She had cuddled and rocked the kitten, cooing as if her were a real baby, and Ray knew she loved him dearly.

When Lottie heard his tale, she said, "I'm sorry, Ray. I loved the little fellow, but we couldn't have him chasing the chickens. You did the right thing. I'm just glad I didn't see you do it—I'm glad Hortense didn't either. Wouldn't she have had a fit! Let's not tell her—maybe she will think he just wandered away."

Ray agreed with instant relief.

Lottie was still worried about Hortense's condition. Dr. Roods had said something mysterious the other day that puzzled her and made her wonder if Hortense would ever recover fully from the surgery. Somehow she got the impression that he had found some other terrible malady besides the appendicitis—maybe it was cancer, Lottie feared. At any rate he had refused to discuss it further, and she was left in the dark. Now that she had become so fond of the child and considered her a real daughter, she certainly didn't want to lose her to some dreadful disease.

She wondered how Stanley could have gone to that silly "Snakes" meeting at the Holden House in Saratoga, while his wife was still so sick. When he came in singing lustily, she realized that he must have had several beers. Just once more before he moved away from Saratoga for good, he wanted to see his old Spanish-American War buddies in the "Military Order of Serpents." She supposed it was all right for them to get together after the national veterans convention and put on a "Bean Feed," wearing those outlandish costumes of theirs. But while Hortense was still in the hospital, how could he have cavorted around so and gotten drunk?

All she said to him when he came in was, "How was Hortense today, Son?"

"Not so good, Ma," he answered, sobering quickly. "She was real depressed and sad and like that. 'Gu Gu Grandississimo' Fred Dunson said he'd go over t' see her t'morrow. He didn't know she was sick 'til I saw him down t' the meeting."

The silly title disgusted Lottie. She couldn't understand how grown men could think up such foolishness. She wondered whether Hortense would appreciate a visit from the "Gu Gu Grandississimo" in her weakened condition.

"That's nice of him to visit her," she said, trying to keep her disapproval from showing in her expression.

Stanley noticed her scornful look though. Disturbed about some inner thoughts, he swayed and almost lost his balance. Opening his mouth as if to tell his mother some solemn secret, he belched loudly instead.

" 'Scuse me."

Then he slurred defensively, "Fred's a good guy. M'bes' buddy. Yessir, he's a nice fella."

Friday September 6th was a very special day. Lottie was bustling around getting the house ready for Hortense's grand homecoming. Stanley had gone down to Saratoga early and would ride back in style in the Durkee's automobile, since they had kindly offered to bring Hortense home.

Soon the touring car pulled up with Elmer and Luella waving triumphantly.

"Here we are back again, minus the appendix!" Elmer called.

"Welcome the returning bride!" Stanley exclaimed, as Elmer braked to a stop by the porch steps.

Lottie beamed joyfully, as she came out on the porch to meet them.

"I'm so glad you're home, Hortense, dear. It's wonderful to see you well again!"

Hortense beamed back at Lottie just as happily. She was sitting up and looked pale and thin, but the pain was gone out of her eyes. Stanley and Elmer carried her together up the stairway.

"Dr. Roods said for Hortense not to walk up or down stairs for at least a week," Luella said aside to Lottie. "He said to keep her on a soft diet until about Tuesday or Wednesday. Then she can eat anything she wants. She doesn't look like the same girl who left here a week and a half ago, does she?"

"Oh my, no, Luella. I was afraid she was going to die before you could get her to the hospital."

"So was I."

Hortense leaned back luxuriously on the pillows.

"It's so good to be home again," she sighed, smiling at everyone contentedly.

"Welcome home, dear," Lottie said. "You certainly look much better than you did when you left here!"

Maybe Dr. Roods was mistaken about Hortense having something else wrong. Doctors can make mistakes, Lottie thought. She didn't want to put any blame on Dr. Roods for not recognizing Hortense's appendicitis sooner. After all he had diagnosed it in time to save her life—though just barely. Doctors really shoulder a great responsibility, she mused. Maybe some patients actually die because of a doctor's error. People put so much faith and trust in doctors, but they are human too, and they can't see inside our bodies to see what is wrong with us when we are ill. She shuddered. Wouldn't it have been terrible if Hortense had died?

Stanley flitted around like a humming bird, fluffing pillows, tugging the bedcovers this way and that, opening the windows a little higher. The nervous concern he had showed during the crucial part of her illness was replaced now by a cheerful, beaming optimism.

"We gotta feed this girl and fatten her up," he chirped. "Doc said give her lotsa milk, chicken soup and soft food f'r the next few days. She'll be good as new before you know it."

The Durkees stayed a few minutes and offered to run any errands for Lottie. With Ray away at the Warrensburg Fair, they knew Stanley wasn't going to budge away from his invalid wife.

Three days later Mame King came trotting up the side porch steps, carrying a small package and a handful of letters.

"Hello, Lottie," she called cheerily. "Perle let me borrow his auto, and I came to see how Hortense is. Brought your mail up as I came—it's all for Hortense and Stanley. How's the patient today?"

"She's much better, Mame. You can go on up if you want to.

She'll be delighted to see you. Ray and Stanley are out picking the Snow apples this afternoon, so she's probably lonely."

"Poor dear. I'll go cheer her up."

She went up the stairway humming a familiar tune. When she got to Hortense's doorway, she burst out with "Happy Birthday."

Hortense laughed delightedly and accepted the little package with surprise. "For *me*?" she asked, as if she didn't know what day it was. She opened it carefully and slowly, so as not to tear the pretty blue tissue. It was a small dresser scarf, embroidered with a basket of lazy daisies in several colors.

"How beautiful!" she exclaimed. "Did you make it, Mame?"

"Yes, indeed I did."

"How sweet of you! Thank you very, very much. You do such beautiful work."

"You're welcome. Now open your mail." she thrust the letters at Hortense.

There was a birthday card from Clif and Mary. Harold had scribbled on the back. Hortense decided it was supposed to be his name. There was another birthday card from Kathleen, Hortense's sister. She had written a letter on the back of it. Hortense told Mame about it.

"Her baby is over two weeks old, Mame. She says they're doin' nicely. Papa moved to Hastin's, Florida two weeks ago, and Mother has gone to join him, now that Kathleen is able to take care of the baby. Mame, I didn't even remember gettin' the letter sayin' that she'd had the baby. The first I knew about it was three or four days after my operation. Stanley said I was delirious when the letter came."

"So I heard. You said all kinds of crazy things. Lottie told me you didn't know anybody for several days."

Hortense read on. Then she looked up with a strange expression.

"Kathleen says they're lookin' for us to come and stay with them in November."

She put the letter down thoughtfully, but without any further comment.

"Here's a letter for Stanley from Atlanta. I think that's Cousin Annie Lawrence's handwritin'. I wonder why she addressed it to Stanley and not to me."

She picked up the next letter. It was a warm, loving letter from her mother and father. They were happy to be together again;

they liked Hastings; Eric had started to school there; and Papa was managing the hardware store. They were so glad to hear that she had improved after her surgery, and they wished her a very happy birthday.

When Stanley came in later and read his letter, he whooped with joy.

"Cousin Annie Lawrence says that Walter might be able t' give me a temporary job in the flower shop this winter. He needs extra help f'r the month of December anyway. Wants me t' come in late November and learn the business so's I can help with the Christmas rush."

Hortense looked at him strangely. "Stanley, did you write and ask them for a job?"

He hung his head sheepishly and said, "Well. . . ."

"But what about your job in Hastin's?"

"They wouldn't hold it f'r me, baby. Said I had t' be there by September third, or else they'd hire someone t' replace me. Doc said you couldn't travel f'r at least a month." He paused and then added gently, "I couldn't go without you."

"My illness made you lose your job! I'm so ashamed! I didn't even realize! Oh, Stanley, I'm so sorry!"

"You were too sick t' realize, sweetie. Don't worry. I'll find a good job in Atlanta."

"You mean we're goin' to live in Atlanta instead of Hastin's?"

"Yep. Atlanta's a growing city. Hub of the south. Railroads going all directions. That's the place t' find a good job. I'll work in the flower shop as long as Walter needs me, then find something else. Atlanta's a good place t' live. You'll be near your sister too."

"But . . ." Hortense hesitated. She didn't want to sound like a baby, but suddenly she felt very insecure, in spite of her ripe old age of twenty. "But Mother and Papa are in Hastin's now."

"Yes, I know, Tiny, but there are no jobs in Hastings. It's such a small town. All's I can do is go where I c'n find work. I think you'll like Atlanta. They say the climate's very good. And you'll get t' see your new nephew."

Hortense couldn't resist that last plea.

"I *am* excited about seein' the baby," she admitted. "Maybe I can help take care of him sometimes. And I want to have a baby too—just as soon as I'm well enough."

She reached over and squeezed Stanley's hand.

"Wherever you are is where I want to be, darlin'. If you say we're goin' to Atlanta, then that's where we're goin'. That's all settled. Don't you think that will be grand, Mame?" she asked brightly.

Mame smiled and agreed that it would indeed be grand.

Sauntering to the clothes press, Stanley came back with two small parcels wrapped in tissue paper.

"Happy Birthday, sweetie."

She opened the packages meticulously.

"Peppermints! You know what I love! And violet toilet water—my favorite!" she exclaimed. "Thank you, Stanley. You're so sweet!"

He grinned with pleasure.

"Well, if we're giving out birthday presents now, I have one for you," said Lottie in the doorway.

She brought in the set of four pillowcases she had embroidered. "This is a wedding and birthday present combined. Happy birthday, dear." Lottie had made them with a feeling of obligation, but now she gave them with much love and affection.

"Oh, Mother Bush, they're beautiful—thank you so much. I'll treasure them always. Did you see the dresser scarf Mame gave me?"

Lottie smiled. "Mame has been working on it almost all summer. She hid it when you were around."

Ray had heard the conversation from his room, and brought in a pretty lace-trimmed handkerchief.

"This is for you, Hortense. Happy birthday."

He looked directly into her brown eyes, as he spoke. She felt that at last he had accepted her into the family.

Smiling warmly she said, "Thank you, dear Ray. What a wonderful family I have."

Ray's heart turned over. She had called him *dear!* How he loved those brown eyes and that sweet smile! If only she were his wife, instead of Stanley's!

Lottie felt gratified that Ray had at last accepted Hortense as his sister. She noticed a real warmth in his smile.

"Something smells mighty good, Ma. What're you baking?"

"That's a sponge cake for Hortense's birthday. I thought that might agree with her better than apple or chocolate cake."

"Oh, what a grand birthday! All these presents and letters and cake too!" Hortense was elated. "You're all so wonderful, and I'm

118

so happy! If I live to be eighty years old I don't think I'll ever have a nicer birthday than this!"

Her recuperation was slow, but in a week or so Hortense was able to manage the stairs and come down for her meals. With Lottie's help she even started some embroidery. But then for several days she felt worse and stayed in bed. Besides the weather had turned cold and disagreeable, and she had no warm clothes to wear. She let Stanley pamper her and bring up her meals again.

At last one morning Stanley didn't come back as usual after breakfast. He and Ray had gone out to look for the buck—he had gotten out of the fence somehow and run away. Hortense crawled out of bed and made the effort to go downstairs to find out what was going on—why Stanley hadn't come back for her breakfast tray as usual.

Lottie heard Hortense's light, slow steps coming down the stairs, and turned from the fresh pork she was cutting up to put in brine.

"Good morning, Hortense. How nice to see you downstairs again. It's been lonely down here these last few days when you've stayed in bed. I'm sorry I've been so busy I haven't spent much time with you. Are you feeling better?"

"Oh, yes, Mother Bush, thank you. I feel much better. I've been huddling under the bed covers to keep warm, but it isn't quite as cold today. It looks like I'll have to buy a warm coat or suit pretty soon."

Looking a little puzzled, she asked, "Is the sun brighter than usual today? Or does it just seem brighter to me because I feel better?"

Instead of answering, Lottie took her arm and said, "Come out here on the porch, dear."

Hortense's eyes seemed to grow bigger in astonishment. Her face took on a rosy tint. The whole area glowed with an unbelievable warmth, as the morning sun shone on the maples surrounding the house. Hortense had always lived in Florida, and she had never seen a northern autumn before. She had never dreamed of anything so beautiful and was too awed to speak for a few minutes. Overwhelmed and dazed, she looked from one tree to another trying to believe the many shades of red, yellow, scar-

119

let, gold, orange, and crimson. The reflections from the trees made the white house look pink.

Lottie pulled her arm gently so that she turned toward the mountain.

"Now look at Mount McGregor."

"Oh, Mother Bush, the whole mountain's on fire!"

"It's magnificent, isn't it? This is my favorite time of the year. Autumn is spectacular in this part of New York. While you've been recuperating upstairs, Jack Frost has been busy painting the leaves."

"I've never seen anything like this before! Is it always so beautiful?"

"It's always different, but always beautiful. I think each year is more gorgeous than the year before."

"Those green spots on the mountain must be the hemlocks Stanley showed me last summer—and the white pines. Everything else looks like a big fire with red embers and yellow flames!"

She looked toward the barn and then walked carefully down the porch steps.

"I'm goin' to walk to the barn and back, Mother Bush. I think I'm strong enough now. I have to drink in as much of this wonderful color as I possibly can, so I'll remember it always. It isn't like this in the south."

"I'll go with you, dear, in case you feel weak."

From the barn Hortense could look back at the house with the cluster of maples forming a brilliant canopy over it. In the opposite direction she could see the cattle grazing in the rolling meadow, a pastoral picture framed by bright golds, reds, and greens of distant forests. She turned in the direction of Wilton and gazed at the tawny fields of corn, no longer fresh and green, as she had last seen them.

Alban whinnied softly. Hortense hadn't seen him come and poke his head curiously over the fence toward her. She rubbed his nose gingerly. The inquisitive cows came ambling over to the fence and stared at her with their enormous, liquid eyes. They seemed to be asking where she had been for so long. A thrush sang his joyful melody.

A warm feeling of peace came over her—an exquisite feeling of fulfillment and bliss.

"How glad I am to be alive! Mother Bush, I love it here! I love

'The Gables' and you and everybody here in Will-ton. I wish we could stay here forever. But I've been so much trouble to you! I know you'll be glad when I leave, but Dr. Roods says I must stay at least another month and gain my strength back."

"You haven't been any trouble at all, dear Hortense. You're the daughter I never had, and I'll miss you terribly when you leave. You know, my dear, for a while I thought you were going to die, and I was out of my mind with worry. I thought I was going to lose the lovely new daughter that I'd grown to love so much."

A wonderful bond of friendship had been established because of that terrible ordeal. They walked back to the house arm in arm.

Lottie was sure now that Stanley had made a good choice after all, and she hoped the marriage would be a lasting one. Hortense seemed so well—surely she wasn't going to die of cancer. Dr. Roods' gloomy suggestion must have been a misunderstanding.

Mary and Harold came to spend a week, so Mary could help Lottie with the grape jelly. It meant taking Harold out of school for a week, but he had been so unhappy and rebellious lately that Mary thought it best to give him a vacation from school.

After Ray left in the wagon with 42 baskets of grapes for Van Deusen's store in Saratoga, Harold started following Grandma around as she cleaned and straightened the house.

"Tell me all about school, Harold," Lottie suggested. "You've hardly told me anything at all."

Harold hung his head and didn't answer right away. Usually he bubbled over with the news of whatever happened to him or wherever he had been. Lottie didn't understand why he was reluctant to talk about school. He had been at the farm for two days and hadn't once mentioned it. Before school started in early September he had been so eager to go. Now after three weeks he seemed disillusioned. Harold frowned gloomily.

Finally he said, "Aw, I guess school isn't so great, after all, Gramma."

"Why, Harold? What's wrong?"

"Nothing."

"Don't you like your teacher?"

"Yes, she's real nice."

"You like your primer, I know. You showed me what a nice

121

book it is with such pretty drawings. I know you were so anxious to learn to read."

"I'm not going t' learn t' read—ever," he said petulantly.

"I don't understand, dear. Why do you say that?"

"I guess I'm just too dumb to learn," he sighed.

"Well, I certainly don't believe that. You're a bright, intelligent and courageous boy. You can learn anything you set your mind to. I have faith in you, Harold. I know you're going to learn to read and write as well as anybody."

Harold tilted his head to one side and studied her face.

"Do you really think so, Gramma?" he asked earnestly.

"I certainly do!" she answered in a firm voice.

Harold looked confused, as if he didn't know what to believe. Finally he began to talk. His words stumbled over each other and turned to sobs.

"One of the boys at school said I was dumb. He called me a cripple. He said cripples don't belong at school. He laughed at me and said I'd never learn anything!"

All this came out in a tearful torrent. Lottie hugged him close to her. He was sobbing into her apron.

"We're going to have to prove to that boy that he was mistaken. You're going to be the best reader in the whole school. There's nothing whatever wrong with your brain, and there's no reason why you shouldn't be in school. Having crippled legs shouldn't keep you from learning anything you want to learn or doing anything you want to do. That boy doesn't understand. I've known you for all of your six years, and I know what a brave boy you are. Just don't pay any attention to him if he talks like that again. You're going to beat him in learning to read and write. You must study hard and do your very best all the time. I believe in you, Harold."

Harold wiped his tears on her apron.

"If he says that again, I'm going t' hit him!" He put up his fists and took a swing at his imaginary enemy. "I'm strong in my arms. I c'n beat him up."

"No, Harold, that isn't the way to act. Many people make cruel remarks without thinking, and we must try not to let them affect us. Sometimes it's very hard to keep from fighting back, but you must be kind to everyone, even the little boy who said those things to you. Kindness brings out kindness in other people. Some day he'll find out what a grand person you are, and he'll realize that he was mistaken."

I should've thought of that when Hortense first came here! The thought came as a surprise to Lottie. Here I am advising Harold, and I didn't even take my own advice! Now I know what a grand person she is, but she is the one who had to teach me to be kind.

Harold was impressed by her profound maxim.

"It's hard t' be kind t' someone who isn't kind t' me, but I'll try, Gramma. I promise."

The next day was fair, and Harold helped his uncles pick grapes.

Mary was helping Lottie can pears, while Hortense watched, feeling rather useless. Her illness had prevented her from learning very much about cooking and canning. While they worked, Mary told her mother-in-law that she had overheard her conversation with Harold the day before.

"I'm so glad you got him to talk about it, Mother Bush. I knew something was bothering him. He was too upset to go to school, but he wouldn't tell me about it. I decided to keep him out this week, hoping some time here on the farm would be good for him. School seemed to have a frightful effect on him."

"Poor little boy. I had so hoped he would enjoy school! He has a terrible burden to bear. I only hope that he will be a stronger and better person when he grows up for going through this ordeal while he's young."

"Thank you for talking to him the way you did. I knew if anyone could help him, you could. I believe he learns more here on the farm from you and Ray than he learns in school anyway."

"That may be true in some ways, Mame, but he must learn to adjust to children his own age. He must get all the book-learning he can too. I hope he'll be happy in school hereafter."

"So do I, Mother Bush." breathed Mary.

Hortense interrupted their conversation.

"I'm goin' to walk over to the hill where the men are pickin' grapes. I need to get some fresh air."

"Do you want me to walk with you?" Mary asked.

"Oh, no thanks. I'll be fine."

In the vineyard she saw the big clusters of purple Concord grapes hanging half-hidden amidst golden leaves all along the rows. She sniffed that delicious scent and said, "Mmm—they smell wonderful!"

Harold pulled her along the ridge.

"Come over here, Aunt Hortense. This is where you c'n hear the echo. Listen."

He began to call in his lusty young voice. "HELLO!"

He grinned at her when the echo came back softly, "Hello."

"You try it," he insisted.

They called back and forth by turns, until Hortense felt tired and Stanley helped her back to the house to rest.

Ray was bringing the last load of grapes in from the vineyard, when he heard an auto roaring angrily backwards and forwards. He knew immediately that someone was stuck in the mud. All that rain on Monday had left the road a mess. Other cars had been through, but they had churned the mud until it was deep and evil-looking. Ray set his baskets of grapes down in the barn and grabbed up a giant armload of straw. He heard the tires still spinning uselessly, not going anywhere.

He strode down the edge of the road where it was not so muddy. Tossing a little straw just in front of each wheel, he suggested that the driver ease forward slowly instead of racing the motor and making the tires spin. The car moved forward a few inches, grinding the straw into the deep mud. Then it was hopelessly stuck again.

"Wait just a minute," Ray called, as he gathered some of the brush and sticks that were in the ditch alongside the road.

He laid several sticks and an armload of brush in front of each tire. The driver eased forward again, and stuck fast, as before.

By this time she had become quite angry. She was an attractive young lady, and it had occurred to Ray that he might be her gallant rescuer and have an excuse to get acquainted with her. He would make her grateful to him for getting her out of the mire; then he would invite her in to have a cup of tea or some of Ma's delicious grape juice and some apple cake. Then he would ask her where she was from. He thought she might live in Glens Falls, since she was headed that way, probably after a trip to Saratoga Springs. In his day-dream she would think he was wonderful and would soon fall in love with him.

In exasperation, the girl wailed, "It's hopeless. I'll never get out of this muck. I'll have to leave my auto here and catch the trolley home."

Ray always managed to do the wrong thing with young ladies,

no matter how well he meant or how hard he tried. He was awkward and self-conscious and his words were invariably fumbling and ill-chosen.

He laughed as he said, "What you need is a h—."

"Sir, how dare you laugh at a lady is distress? You're no gentleman. I've never been so insulted in my life."

As she spoke she climbed out of the car and stepped down from the running board—straight into the mud. She stood mired almost to her boot tops, trying to hold her skirt out of the mud.

Ray's face was burning red. He was apologetic and embarrassed.

"Please, Miss. Stay in your auto, while I hitch up a horse to pull you out. I'll only be a minute. After I get the auto out of the mud, I'll clean your shoes for you. Here, take my handkerchief. That'll help a little."

He ran back to the barn to get Billy and soon was back at the auto. It wasn't difficult for Billy to pull the car past the worst section of the road, so the young lady could drive on again.

"Road's in terrible shape," Ray remarked. "It's a real problem after every rain. Come in the house and you can have a glass of fresh grape juice while I clean off your boots."

"Thanks very much for pulling me out," the girl said frostily. "No, I can't come in. I'm in a hurry. I'm late as it is. Oh, here's your handkerchief."

She handed him the sodden mess that had been his new linen handkerchief and drove off, slithering down the road toward Glens Falls. Ray's daydream had gone the same course as all the others. He had not meant to insult her. He had tried only to be helpful and kind. But he had lost again.

He stomped gloomily up the path to the orchard to check the Spies. Even his fantasy wife, "Eve," couldn't console him this time. He felt crushed by an overwhelming loneliness. An imaginary wife was not enough any longer. He needed someone real and tangible. How he wished Hortense were his wife instead of Stanley's!

# A PERFECT DAY
## Chapter 10

"We'll never have a more gorgeous day than this f'r our trip to Lake George, Tiny. Do you feel like going?" Stanley asked the following Saturday.

"Oh, yes, let's go. I've been lookin' forward to that since last June."

"It'll be the best part of our honeymoon, I promise. Nothing can possibly go wrong t'day."

Ray took them to the trolley stop at Doe's Corner in time for the 9:30 trolley.

As they got on, Hortense said, "This will be the climax of our honeymoon, won't it, darlin'? We'll have a romantic time to remember forever."

They sat holding hands on the long, delightful ride, as they sped along at a breathtaking twenty miles an hour past mountains, farms, and forests ablaze with color. Autumn was spreading its glory on the whole countryside. At Glens Falls, where the through car crossed the Hudson River, more people piled on carrying picnic baskets and calling happily to friends. Several spoke to Stanley, and he introduced his bride.

When the car stopped at Lake George Village, Stanley pulled Hortense over to a high grassy hill. She gasped when she saw the lake shimmering in the sunshine. It was like a huge gem set down between two ridges of mountains, extending far into the distance. At the edge of the lake she saw a wharf with a large steamboat tied.

"Right here's where Fort William Henry used t' be. Massacre here in 1757. . . ."

"Hush, Stanley." Hortense covered her ears with her hands and shuddered. "I don't want to hear any more. I'm not in the mood for your old lectures now—especially not about any massacre."

126

"Okay, let's sit down here in the sunshine, Tiny." He spread a blanket on the ground. "Now sit down. Have you ever seen a prettier sight in your life? Didn't I tell you I'd take you on a beautiful wedding trip? Now at last we'll have our honeymoon! Lake George's the place f'r honeymooners."

Hortense stretched out on the blanket and rested and dozed for a little while, feeling supremely contented. Then they opened the delicious picnic lunch Lottie had made for them.

After they had eaten, they wandered down the hill to Chester B. Smith's shop near the landing and bought postcards to send to Hortense's family.

"Oh, Stanley, may I get this cute little souvenir dish?"

"By golly, of course you can, little lady, and I want this copy of the *Lake George Mirror*. Let's get an ice cream too—wouldn't that taste good?"

So, nibbling the ice cream slowly to make it last a long time, they gathered their purchases into the picnic basket and walked to the landing to catch the steamer. Stanley bought their tickets for seventy-five cents each.

The boat ride was magnificent, and the fresh air was so invigorating that Hortense didn't feel she had ever been sick. The "Whoosh—chuff" of the steam engine startled Hortense at first, but soon became the steady and monotonous breathing of the big *Mohican*. Except when the blast of its loud whistle came at each landing, there was only the quiet slap of the paddle wheel to accompany the continuous "Whoosh-chuff." People got on or off at several landings along the way, and Stanley kept pointing out the summer "cottages" of wealthy people.

"I would call those castles, not cottages!" Hortense exclaimed.

The sun and the wind brought color to Hortense's face and a sparkle to her eyes. A feeling of exhiliration enveloped her that she had never known before. Certainly she had never seen such green water and such a magnificent view.

"What makes the water so green?" she asked.

"The lake is spring fed, baby," he answered, as if that explained everything to her. "Almost no streams flowing int' it t' make it muddy."

At the narrows Hortense felt that she could almost reach out and pick a red maple leaf on one side and a yellow birch leaf on

127

the other at the same time. The wonderful warmth and beauty of the day had a healing effect on her heart, as well as her body.

"Stanley, I've always been afraid of boats because I can't swim, but this time I love it! I've never been on such a big one before. Wouldn't it be wonderful if we could go back to Atlanta by boat, instead of that horrible, dirty old train!"

Stanley cocked his head thoughtfully. "Well, I don't see why we can't, Tiny. I'll check int' that soon. There's steamships from New York City to Savannah. Maybe we could go there and just take the train from Savannah t' Atlanta. That ought t' be a fitting end t' our honeymoon. All the best f'r my beautiful bride! Doc wants you t' wait awhile before you travel such a long way, though. Doesn't think you're strong enough yet."

The boat came back to the landing, and Stanley pointed at the new Fort William Henry Hotel next to the railroad.

"That's where the millionaires stayed on their honeymoons this summer, I'll bet. Fireproof and American Colonial style—spiffy, isn't it?"

"Yes, but not as big as the Grand Union."

Hortense measured everything in comparison with the giant hotels in Saratoga Springs now.

Guiding her back to the grassy hill again, Stanley spread the blanket, so they could enjoy the view a little longer. Hortense squeezed his hand and gave a contented sigh.

"Honey, this is just wonderful! It's a perfect day! My heart is overflowin'! I think I must be the happiest person in the whole wide world! I am so lucky to have you—and so very lucky to be alive!"

Stanley stared down at the grass and didn't answer. Hortense saw that he was troubled.

"What is it, Stanley? Aren't you glad I recovered from my appendicitis?"

"Oh, baby, you know I am! It's just that there's something I must tell you. . . ."

"Well, don't wear such a long face, dear. You can tell me anythin'. What could you possibly have to tell me that would make you sad on such a beautiful day as this?"

"It's something that'll make you sad too, pet. Maybe I should tell you now while you're happy. The longer I wait t' tell you, the harder it gets, but I promised Dr. Roods I'd do it. I didn't want him t' tell you while you were so sick."

"But Stanley, I feel fine. I'm not goin' to die. I'm gettin' better all the time. What do you mean? What did you promise Dr. Roods you'd tell me?"

Stanley still hesitated. It wasn't like him to be at a loss for words. Normally he could talk down any two or three other people. Now it was hard for him to choose the right words to minimize the hurt.

Finally he blurted the truth in a few brief words.

"Doc says you'll never be able t' have babies. When they operated they found the appendix had ruptured. Peritonitis had spread the infection. He said you were pregnant—did you know that? Said there was absolutely no possibility of saving the baby or of you ever getting pregnant again."

Stanley had hoped that she already suspected the truth three weeks ago, but no—the shock on her face was complete. All her dreams of a beautiful little family were squelched in that instant. She couldn't speak for a long time. Then she sat up very straight and issued a simple and courageous statement.

"We have each other, Stanley. That's all that matters. We'll love and cherish each other as long as we live. When I think about how near I came to death, I can't really complain about not being able to have children."

She hesitated. Then very softly she added, "Maybe some day we can adopt a baby and raise it as our own."

Stanley jumped up and shouted explosively, "NO!"

Hortense was startled by his vehemence.

"I will *not* raise a bastard! Nobody c'n ever say, 'There goes that Bush child. They say his mother was a whore and his father was a drunk!' No siree, I'll not have any part of that!"

He shook his head violently, then sat down abruptly and with a remorseful voice he said, "I'm sorry, Tiny. I shouldn't have spoken so rudely, but I feel very strongly about that. Please don't ask me t' consider it."

The anger was gone, and he was all gentleness and concern again. But his penitence came too late. The damage was done. Hortense was stunned by his outburst. How could he say such things to her? Nothing would ever be the same between them again. Not have chidlren—ever?

And what were those horrible words he had spat at her? For the first time Stanley had shown himself to be callous and selfish. Tears choked her and she couldn't speak. Stanley was a stubborn man; he would never change his mind. His decisions were unshakeable, and his word was final. There was nothing she could say—so she said nothing. Stanley saw her silence as acquiescence to his ultimatum.

How could a few simple sentences, spoken in less than five minutes time change her life so much? She had been supremely happy; now she was devastated.

"I know this news is a shock t' you, and I'm sorry. I've wondered for a long time how t' tell you, and I waited until I thought you were too happy t' be sad very long. I feel better now that the secret is no longer a burden to me."

He held her hand lovingly and went on talking, since she still didn't speak to him. "It's been hard t' hold something back from you, sweetie." He chattered on and on about inconsequential matters.

On the ride back, the other young people were jovial. Someone began singing and the others took up the song, "When you come to the end of a perfect day. . . ."

Hortense pretended to be too tired to sing, or even to talk to Stanley all the way home, even though he tried to make her laugh with his usual silly antics. The more he prattled, the more irritated she was.

When he met the 7:30 car at Doe's Corner, Ray noticed that Hortense had been crying. Stanley jabbered about what a glorious day it had been and what fun they had, apparently oblivious to Hortense's somber mood. She is at last beginning to see what an insensitive clod he is, Ray thought.

Lottie wanted to hear all about her impressions of Lake George, but Hortense ran upstairs and went straight to bed. The poor thing is just exhausted, Lottie thought. Stanley effervesced about what a wonderful day they had, but didn't mention his revelation. For some reason he was still reluctant to discuss Hortense's sterility, even with his own mother.

The next day Hortense was subdued and quiet—not her usual vivacious self at all. Lottie watched her anxiously. Was she having a relapse or was she just tired from the trip?

When Ray had gone outside to work and Stanley was puttering

around in the shed, Lottie took advantage of a tranquil time to question Hortense about how she liked Lake George.

"Oh, it was gorgeous, Mother Bush!" Hortense said brightly, but Lottie sensed that her usual gay buoyancy was missing.

She took Hortense's hands and held them gently, while she looked intently into her eyes. Hortense felt that Mother Bush could read her thoughts when she did that. She began to weep, though she tried to blink the tears back. When Lottie said, "What's wrong, Hortense, dear?" the stream flowed like a flood.

"I can't ever have babies, Mother Bush," she stammered. "Didn't Stanley tell you?"

Lottie was as shocked as Hortense had been. Dr. Roods had depended on Stanley to break the news to his family and had only hinted to Lottie about Hortense's problem. Between sobs Hortense managed to tell Lottie the whole story. Lottie's face was wet with tears too, not only in sympathy for her sweet daughter-in-law, but for herself. Now she wouldn't have any more grandchildren. She had so hoped for a little granddaughter.

"Perhaps Stanley will change his mind later and be willing to adopt a child," was the only consolation she could offer, but she didn't really believe he would.

Last year Ray had been able to sell all their apples locally or in Clif's store at Palmer—probably fifty barrels in all. This year there would be far more than the villages of Saratoga Springs, Wilton, Gurn Spring, Palmer, and Corinth could use. Louis Schwarz from the Schwarz Cold Storage Company in Ballston Spa came at Lottie's request and inspected their crop.

After he had walked through all the orchards, he said, "I'll pay $1.50 per barrel for up to 250 barrels, less the shipping charges, Mrs. Bush.

"Let's give them another week to ripen before you start to pick, Ray. Then send me first quality apples. I don't want any seconds, remember. While you're packing, I'll come back to check on how they look—probably in about ten days."

"Plan to stay for dinner that day, Mr. Schwarz," Lottie urged.

"That's very kind of you, Mrs. Bush. I'll be happy to."

When the Staples came to visit later that afternoon, Stanley had to wake Hortense. She had been upstairs resting and had cried herself to sleep, her arms aching to hold a baby like Donald.

131

How many tender moments would she miss in the time it takes an infant to grow to adulthood? How could Stanley be so stubborn and insensitive?

Stanley shook her shoulder gently. She opened her eyes a crack.

"Wake up, little lady. Roger and Ella Staples 're here. They brought Mame King and Ella Thompson with them. C'mon, Sweetie, wake up and come downstairs t' see them."

Hortense yawned and stretched grumpily.

"I guess I fell asleep. I'm kinda groggy—don't feel like bein' polite to anybody, but tell them I'll be down in a few minutes."

Everyone gathered in the kitchen, talking to Lottie while she finished canning the Elberta peaches Ray had bought.

Mame said, "I brought you some magazines, Lottie. They're on the dining room table. I thought you'd be especially interested in the *Scientific American* article about the Panama Canal."

"Indeed I would. Thank you, Mame. Isn't it fantastic that they can cut a continent in half that way? We're certainly living in an exciting modern world, aren't we?"

Everyone chimed an assent.

Hortense came down then and greeted her friends. The crowd moved into the sitting room and discussed everything from the bumper apple crop to the approaching Presidential election.

The many points in favor of each candidate were all explored in good humor, along with the unfavorable points. Woodrow Wilson was much respected, but would he be a strong president? Of course Taft had the advantage of being the incumbent. Roosevelt had an appeal to the common man and had gained much strength since the formation of the "Bull Moose" Party.

The discussion was going briskly when Ray came in from Saratoga and joined in with the latest gossip from Van Deusen's store, where he had taken a wagon load of grapes.

Then Stanley started recounting all the details of their excursion to Lake George and what a marvelous time they had. Hortense smiled rather vacantly, but didn't comment. Her reticence was attributed to fatigue and overstrain. She was relieved when the party broke up.

If only he had a chance to speak to Hortense alone, Ray wanted to tell her how much he sympathized with her in her distress that Ma had confided to him. He noticed the anguish in her eyes when Stanley talked about their "perfect day," and he wished for once in his life to be eloquent in expressing his deepest emotions without stumbling over words. Oh, how he yearned to tell her that he loved her.

About a week later Stanley took Hortense to Saratoga Springs again. She had bravely come to grips with her situation and accepted it as gracefully as possible. Their first quarrel had definitely taken the ecstasy out of her marriage, but there really wasn't much else for her to do but make the best of things. Stanley was a very determined man. There was no point in arguing with him. At least once each day since the trip to Lake George, she had gone into a crying spell, but she tried not to let anyone see. Trying to act enthusiastic about this next outing she soon found herself enjoying it, even though she no longer felt in love with her husband.

They got on the trolley to Saratoga Lake.

"Oh, Stanley, look at the steamboat!" Hortense exclaimed when they reached the lake.

He grinned at her. "I think you're beginning t' like boats. Would you like t' take a ride on the 'Alice'?"

"You know I would."

When they were in the middle of the lake, Stanley pointed out Mount McGregor in the distance, and Hortense said pensively, "Just think, Stanley, last summer we were standin' up there on top of the mountain lookin' down at this lake. That was the most wonderful day of my life."

After the ride, they ate supper at Newman's Lake House, and Stanley prated on and on about Moon's Lake House, the famous home of the potato chip, which used to be nearby.

This time there was no emotional scene to mar the afternoon, but Hortense was more restrained and not as openly affectionate as she had been before. She no longer giggled at Stanley's crazy antics or laughed at his nonsensical conversation. Now she was too old and sedate for that kind of foolishness. Somehow he seemed like a silly schoolboy who had never grown up. His constant patter about nothing annoyed her more and more.

A few days later Hortense started out to walk to the Spy orchard on the mountain, but had to stop to rest in the west vineyard. She was sitting on a patch of grass with a deliciously pleasant sun

133

warming her body. The golden grape leaves stretched way into the distance on both sides of her with a few purple grapes still hiding among the bright leaves. Behind the vineyard the mountain was still glowing like a roaring fire. Sprawling out on the grass, she looked around her and listened to the hum of the cicadas. She glimpsed the apple trees with their branches drooping low from the weight of the apples. Soon Ray and Stanley would start picking the apples, which were ripe and ready.

"If I hadn't gotten sick, I would have missed all this autumn splendor," she murmured. "This is ecstasy!"

She got up and picked some wild asters and goldenrod.

"Mother Bush ought to like these on her table."

Carefully avoiding a bee, she sat down again, and stretching lazily, she tried to imitate the hum of the cicadas; then she buzzed in imitation of the bees. Just then Ray came down the trail and interrupted her contented mood.

"Have you ever seen a more glorious day, Tiny?"

"Never. I was just sitting here thinking that getting sick has its merits. Nothing is ever so bad but what some good comes of it. My illness gave me some time to enjoy life that I would never have had otherwise. I'll keep all these precious moments and beautiful images in my heart for the rest of my life."

She reached out to pick a cluster of grapes and started nibbling them, while Ray nodded in agreement.

"When I'm eighty, and my teeth have fallen out, my eyes have gone blind, and my ears are deaf, I'll still have these wonderful memories to treasure. I can look at these 'pictures' of my honeymoon any time I want to, just by thinkin' about them. Nobody can ever take them away from me. I'll forget the pain and only remember the good parts of my honeymoon."

Ray was smiling at her eloquence.

"You know, Ray, I'm really very lucky. I love it so much here on the farm—in Saratoga—with you and Mother Bush. It's all so wonderful, I wish I never had to leave!"

Ray wanted to be able to express himself as well as Hortense.

"Most people wouldn't count themselves lucky when they had almost died the way you did."

"If I hadn't gotten sick, it would have been the most glorious honeymoon a girl ever had. As it is—well, I'm just lucky to be alive. Of course I do wish I could have at least one baby, but that will never be now," she said morosely.

"You could adopt a baby, Hortense."

"That's what I thought too, but Stanley won't hear of it, so that's the end of it."

"I don't think Stanley should make that decision without considering your wishes. He's not being fair to you."

"I don't think he's bein' fair either. Sometimes I hate him." Her voice began to tremble. "In fact I can't remember now why I fell in love with him, anyway—just loneliness at the time, I guess."

Tears began to run down her face. Ray took her hand in his big paw.

"I'm sorry I upset you so, but I really believe that Stanley is wrong to keep you from having the family you yearn to have."

"Oh, Ray, what am I goin' to do? Sometimes I get so irritated with him. He doesn't consider my feelings at all."

"I know, dear. He can be very infuriating." Ray squeezed her hand tenderly. There were so many things he wanted to say, but he couldn't make the words come.

"I guess I'll just have to make the best of it. He's still my husband, and I must respect his wishes."

"You're a wonderful person, Hortense. I think Stanley should respect your wishes."

"Thank you, Ray. I think you're wonderful too, and I love you very much. You're so strong and handsome, I can't imagine why some smart girl hasn't married you by now."

She patted his hand, picked up her flowers, and stood up, bravely trying to put an end to the emotional scene. Before she could turn away, Ray grabbed her forcefully and kissed her, gently in the beginning, then with a crushing urgency. She responded at first, but suddenly broke away.

"Oh, Ray—we mustn't!"

She ran back toward the house, her heart pounding and her face burning with shame at what she had done. She had admired, even idolized Ray for some time, but hadn't realized until this moment that she was falling in love with him!

Slowing to a walk, she tried to gain control of her breathing, so Stanley wouldn't suspect anything untoward. Then she stopped in the yard, puzzling over what Stanley was building.

"What's that, Stanley?"

"Well, now, it's a table t' sort apples on, Tiny," he said with a grin. "Have t' pack 'em by size. Get better prices f'r the big ones."

"I see," she said doubtfully. "I'm goin' to take these flowers to your mother."

"Okay, baby. You feeling all right?"

"Sure, I'm fine—just a little tired."

When Ray came by a few minutes later and saw Stanley's new invention, he snorted in aggravation. In the time it had taken him to build the table he could have sorted six barrels of apples. Stanley always had to waste time on absurd and worthless nonsense. He would spend a lot of time rolling the apples back and forth on the table trying to decide what size they were, when he could have just picked them up from the baskets and put them directly into barrels. No use trying to tell Stanley how to do it, though. He would try to be grateful for his help. When Stanley's gone, he resolved, I'll chop his fancy sorting table up into firewood.

This was the finest apple crop Ray could ever remember. He had hired Tabe Washburn and Carl and Clifford Wentworth to help him pick, and they were all busy out in the orchards. The boys felt free to bite into a juicy, tart-sweet apple whenever they were hungry or thirsty. None of the apples had ever been sprayed, and their flavor right off the trees was superb.

While Ray picked methodically and carefully, he brooded about poor Hortense. She was too wonderful a girl to have to suffer all her life because of her mistake in marrying that irritating idiot, Stanley. If Stanley hadn't married her, she wouldn't have gotten pregnant—she wouldn't have had appendicitis—and she wouldn't be faced with a barren life ahead of her.

He began to try to think of a way to solve her dilemma. If only something would happen to Stanley—then she would be free! Of course she might divorce him—no, he didn't think she would agree to that, no matter how much she wanted to be rid of him. She had said something once about how much she disapproved of divorce.

Wouldn't it be justice if Stanley should be up on a high ladder like this one and just happen to fall and break his head open and die? He deserved to die! Of all the bull-headed, aggravating dolts he was the worst. What right did he have to ruin a beautiful girl's future?

Ray began to imagine Stanley up in one of the tallest trees, reaching for an apple on the end of a limb and falling unconscious to the ground, his neck broken and his head hanging limp and lifeless. He would offer Hortense his deepest sympathy and concern. After a time—a few months, maybe, she would realize that it was Ray she truly loved, and she would whisper, "Yes, oh, yes, darlin'," when he asked her to marry him.

Just then a rung on the ladder broke, and Ray slithered to the ground, scratched on one cheek and embarrassed, but otherwise unhurt. He took the ladder to Ross in Wilton to be mended, angry with himself for being overweight. When he got home he washed out a hundred more barrels, so they would be ready for use.

Hortense was stimulated by the bustle and activity of the harvest. The fresh air was invigorating, and the delicate, but pervasive scent of apples was pleasantly appetizing. She was healthy and rosy-cheeked now, but the buoyancy of her personality was gone. She walked and talked more sedately than before her illness. Her response to Stanley's palaver was usually chilly.

On Sunday afternoon all the neighbors went to Grant Cottage to meet Mrs. Clarke's sister, Dr. Kelsey, who was here for a visit. Ray brought along the four barrels of apples that Mr. Clarke had ordered—three for the Sanatorium workers and one special barrel of Spies for themselves.

At the door Lottie exclaimed, "The new macadam road is wonderful! You won't have any more trouble getting stuck on the mountain road!"

"Yes, aren't we lucky? But where are Hortense and Stanley?" Mrs. Clarke wanted to know.

"Hortense would have been here, if she'd had her way. They were also invited to a dance in Glens Falls, and I overheard them arguing about which party to attend."

"Oh, a little lovers' quarrel, eh?"

"I'm afraid so. Hortense was pouting and sulking when she left home, but she won't pout long."

Dr. Kelsey had many interesting experiences to relate about her work as a medical missionary in Japan. Another stimulating guest was Miss Robbins, from the Metropolitan office in New York City. She had come to inspect the sanatorium construction and consider the position of head nurse. The little group was eager

137

to hear all the information she could give them about the way the sanatorium would operate.

"The two main buildings and two ward buildings should be finished in about four months, but it will probably be at least eight months before all the doctors, nurses, clerical, and maintenance people can be chosen. Notices will go out soon to all employees of the Metropolitan Life Insurance Company throughout the United States, saying that patients can be accepted late next summer."

Lottie asked, "Do you suppose we could tour all the buildings when they're finished? I'm sure they won't let us in after the patients arrive, but I'd like to see the furnishings and all."

"Oh, yes. They're going to have an Open House and invite everyone in the community to inspect the buildings, inside and out."

There were murmurs of approval at that. Everyone was flattered that a large company like the Metropolitan was considerate enough to invite their inspection.

When Grace and John Myers came in, bringing their baby and a freezer of peach ice cream, they soon became the center of attention. The ice cream was quickly disposed of by eager tasters. The baby was passed from one lap to another, gurgling happily. Donald was seven months old now—a jolly, good-natured baby.

"What do you think Donald will be when he grows up, Grace?"

"I think he'd make a fine governor of New York, Mrs. Clarke," Grace answered laughing.

Their friends began speculating on what career he might follow. John insisted that Donald would be a good farmer.

"What could be better than that? It's farmers that feed the nation."

"You're right, John, farming is a grand occupation, but I feel that Donald has some very special, illustrious future before him. With such fine parents he is bound to be successful."

They would all remember the next Tuesday as the day Ray had hiccoughs all afternoon. He came in for a lot of kidding about that, especially since he was not a drinking man. All the men at the store teased him about being drunk, but the news of the day was far from funny. That was the day everybody heard that Teddy Roosevelt had been shot the night before—right before he was to

138

make a campaign speech in Milwaukee. The conversation down at Van Rensselaer's was tense.

"Bullet lodged in the wall of his chest!"

"Lucky for him it hit the manuscript of his speech first!"

"Paper said he refused t' go t' the hospital. Said, 'I will make this speech or die—one or the other.' "

"I heard that he also said, 'It takes more than that t'kill a Bull Moose.' "

When Dan McNeal came by the house for his bushel of apples, he told Lottie all about it. Then he had a laugh over Ray's hiccoughs. A little later Ralph Clements came for his bushel of grapes and went through the same spiel.

"Do you suppose more people will vote for Roosevelt out of sympathy?" Lottie asked.

"Hard to tell. Anything's possible in this election, I'd say."

Even more startling to the Bushes than the news from Milwaukee was the drama that took place in the kitchen that evening.

After supper, Hortense carefully cleaned and polished the chimney of the lantern with a piece of old newspaper. Then she lighted the lantern and picked it up to take with her on one last visit to the water closet. Just as she reached to open the door, somehow she tripped, and the lantern fell to the floor on its side. Kerosene spilled out and flared up.

Hortense screamed, 'Fire!" just as she had screamed in the burning barn last summer.

Stanley leaped to her side, grabbed the lantern and threw it outside in one rapid motion. Lottie threw her dishpan of water on the flaming pool on the lineoleum almost at the same moment.

In less than half a minute all the excitement was over, and no harm was done, except that the lantern was broken. Lottie mopped up the puddle of water. They all stood there talking at once and breathing sighs of relief.

"What if the house had burned down!" Lottie exclaimed, her fear of house fires always foremost in her mind.

"Were you burned, Tiny?" Stanley asked anxiously.

"I'm so sorry I caused so much trouble. It was my fault," Hortense sobbed tearfully. She assured Stanley that she wasn't hurt—just scared.

"You're real lucky you weren't burned, Hortense," Ray said

solicitously. He realized more and more that he was very much in love with his brother's wife. In the perversity of human nature, he had changed over a period of a few weeks from hatred and resentment to passionate love. All of his fantasies now centered around Hortense and his whole body ached to hold her and kiss her again and to tell her how much he loved her.

# INDIAN SUMMER
## Chapter 11

Giggling at her ludicrous image in the mirror, Hortense put on Stanley's jacket over Lottie's sweater before she ventured out to help Lottie dig bulbs. It was the sixteenth of October, and the houseplants had frozen on the side porch, even though Lottie had covered them with a blanket. Clifford Wentworth dug potatoes all day, while the other hired boys kept on picking apples. Hortense helped Lottie pull the carrots, beets, and gladiolus bulbs. They had become close and loving companions.

"When we move to Atlanta, will you write to me, Mother Bush? I feel so afraid to face a new life without the comfort of your help and advice."

"Of course I will, dear. You must write me all about your life in Atlanta, and I'll tell you all about what we're doing here on the farm."

"I love you so much, Mother Bush—I hate to think of leavin' here!"

Lottie thought she saw Hortense's chin quiver just a little.

"I'm going to miss you terribly, my dear. It will be lonely here after you and Stanley move away."

"Oh, Mother Bush, I do wish we didn't have to go to Atlanta. It's so big and noisy."

"But I thought you were excited about going there and seeing your sister's baby and all."

"I was excited for a while—now I'm just scared. What if Stanley can't find a permanent job? Kathleen won't want us stayin' there indefinitely—she only invited us for the month of December. Cousin Annie doesn't have room for us. What will we do if Stanley can't find a job after Christmas?"

It sounded like Hortense didn't have a lot of confidence in Stanley's work potential after having watched him work on the farm, Lottie thought.

"Atlanta is such a thriving city—surely there must be plenty of jobs. You mustn't worry about that, Hortense."

"I suppose you're right, as usual, Mother Bush," Hortense sighed. "I just wish we could stay here."

Lottie gave her a hug. "I'm glad you like us well enough to want to stay here."

Privately she was thinking how disastrous that would be to have Stanley and Ray trying to share the farm work on a permanent basis. How many times they had quarreled as they were growing up! How many times she had feared for Stanley's life when they fought, because Ray was always so much larger and stronger! She was grateful that they had curbed their hostility this year, but wasn't sure how long their truce would last. She had observed several confrontations and seen that Ray turned and walked away without a word.

No, it would be much better for Hortense and Stanley to go away and become independent. Lottie felt much more optimistic about their chances of saving their marriage away from Saratoga. Hortense is a strong and courageous young woman, Lottie thought. I believe she has enough determination to make Stanley behave himself and settle down into a decent, hard-working husband. Maybe they can find happiness—even without children. As soon as they get settled and find a job in Atlanta, I think their problems will be solved.

At the end of the day Saturday, Clifford Wentworth asked Lottie if he could have part of his pay, so she reached into her sugar bowl and pulled out eight one-dollar bills and $2 in silver.

"Here's $10 on account, Clifford. We owe you $2 more now for the twelve days you've worked so far. I'll pay that with the rest of your salary when we're through with the apple harvest."

"Thanks, Mrs. Bush. I have t' get some things at the store, so I appreciate you letting me have this advance."

"You're very welcome, dear. You're such a wonderful help to us—you're just like a member of the family. I miss you when you go back to your own home."

"Thank you, ma'am. I'll be back Monday morning. I'm already looking forward to some more of your apple cake and deep-dish apple pie with cream."

He rode off toward Wilton on his bicycle, leaving Lottie beaming after him.

All of the hired boys were "her boys." She mothered them, loved them, fed them until they couldn't hold another bite, and treated them as part of her own family. If they had any problems, they knew they could count on Lottie for help. Usually they stayed at "The Gables" through the week during harvest season, taking Sunday off to be with their own families.

A little later when John Nichols came by for some buttermilk, Lottie was overjoyed to see him.

"I've missed you so much this year, John. Ray had hoped to get you to help us with the harvest again this year, but found that you weren't at home."

"Yes, ma'am, Ma told me he came by asking for me, but I'm living in Saratoga Springs now—going to high school."

"I think that's wonderful, dear. I'm really proud of you. I'm sure you'll be a very successful man when you finish school."

They chatted for a few minutes about the crops and reminisced about his years as a hired boy on the farm.

"Do you remember the time I spent the night up in the apple tree to watch for the raccoons that were getting your corn?"

"Indeed I do," Lottie laughed. "You shot three that night, and we haven't seen a raccoon since."

She was still smiling as John walked down the road, carrying his jug of buttermilk.

It was the last week in October, and there was a haze of Indian Summer on the mountain. The baskets and barrels of apples sitting here and there in the yard, in the sheds, on the porches, and in the orchards gave off that tantalizing odor. The kitchen almost always had apple pies, cakes, or sauce adding to the fragrance outdoors. Bees and birds came to help the pigs in the job of cleaning up the discarded apples on the ground.

Ray and Stanley were finally ready to load the boxcar going to Schwarz in Ballston Spa. It was a strain for Alban and Billy to pull the heavy wagon loaded with sixteen barrels of apples, but on Friday they made six trips to the railroad siding near Van Rennselaer's store. Roy grunted as he hoisted each barrel from the wagon to the freight car. Then Stanley rolled it deftly into place inside the car.

143

Ray had figured on climbing up inside the boxcar and letting Stanley pass the barrels up to him. He was thinking that if a barrel accidentally slipped and fell back on Stanley, it would crush him to the ground. It might even kill his obnoxious brother. But when they pulled the wagon up beside the car, it was Stanley that leaped up quickly and said, "You pass 'em up t' me, Ray." Ray would have to think of some better way to get rid of Stanley.

It took four more trips on Saturday to fill the first boxcar with 159 barrels of apples that would bring $6 to $7 a barrel in the big city markets.

Lottie and Hortense had gone shopping in Glens Falls and bought some lovely blue flannel for night robes. The cold nights really made Hortense long for something warm to wear. Getting out of bed in the morning was a dreaded experience. Hortense was not much of a seamstress, but with Lottie's help, she managed to make bathrobes for herself and Stanley. Since Hortense's illness, Lottie had been happy to teach her any housekeeping skills she requested. It seemed strange now that she had been so resentful of the girl before her illness. They were just finishing the last seams when Ray and Stanley brought in the mail.

Lottie was delighted to find a package from Mary containing 100 new Victor fibre needles for the talking machine. Each one would play eight records before having to be sharpened, and she immediately tried one on Mary's favorite song, "Down by the Old Mill Stream." It did give a much truer sound, she thought.

She perused Mary's letter, anxious to know how Clif's little family was. Satisfied that all was well with them, she got up and put another record on the gramophone.

Stanley hummed along as the big, blue speaker crooned romantically, ". . . You have stolen my heart, now don't go 'way, As we sang love's old sweet song on Moonlight Bay."

"I won't go 'way, Tiny," Stanley assured Hortense, coming up behind her and giving her a hug. "It's been a week now since I wrote t' the Ocean Steamship Company. We should hear soon about our reservations for Georgia."

He kissed her cheek. "Won't that be romantic t' sail f'r three days 'n' nights? I hope the moon'll be full!"

"I'm afraid it will be stormy," she answered morosely. "Maybe we shouldn't go by ship after all."

"But we've already paid for the tickets. I'm sure you'll love it, sweetie. Don't worry."

A week later the apple harvest was finished and Lottie was calculating what their income would be. They had shipped a total of 224 barrels to Schwarz at $1.50 per barrel. Subtracting $20 for the shipping charges and $52.24 for the hired boys, she came up with a profit of $263.76. She jotted all the figures down in her diary, feeling unusually wealthy.

Stanley burst into the kitchen full of excitement.

"Listen t' this, folks! We're going t' sail from New York aboard the *City of St. Louis* on Thursday, November 21 at 3:00 p.m. and arrive at Savannah on Sunday, November 24. Fare's only $25. 'A smooth sail o'er Pleasant Seas,' it says here."

He grabbed Hortense and started dancing around the kitchen with her.

"How does that sound t' you, Tiny?"

"It sounds nice," she answered vaguely, "but the weather will probably be cold and miserable."

"We'll have a romantic cruise t' top off our honeymoon trip. Stay a couple days in Savannah—I've never seen Savannah, have you? Catch a train overnight t' Atlanta. Settle in with Kathleen and Russel. Be ready t' go t' work f'r Walter Lawrence on December 2. We c'n look around f'r an apartment after we get there."

Stanley danced Hortense around crazily until she was out of breath. She looked pained by his idiotic horseplay.

"That makes me dizzy, Stanley," she said irritably.

Lottie observed the change in Hortense's reaction to Stanley's antics with alarm. Stanley was being ridiculous, but no more so than usual, and Hortense had loved it before. Now suddenly Hortense was acting more mature and was offended by his childishness. Previously Lottie had felt that their marriage couldn't last because of Hortense's immaturity and youth. Now she was worried about their marriage because Stanley was acting so immature. With a feeling of shock, Lottie realized that if the two of them should break up, she would prefer to keep Hortense. Let Stanley leave and seek his fortune elsewhere—Lottie loved her daughter-in-law.

Next Tuesday would be election day, the day people all across the land had been anticipating for months. But the flag at the

145

post office was flying at half-mast—Vice-President James School-
craft Sherman was dead. Everyone felt peculiar, as well as sad,
because it meant that many men would be voting for a dead man
on Tuesday. There wasn't time for the Republican National Com-
mittee to select a new candidate and put his name on the ballot.
They had announced a meeting for November to select a new
running mate for President Taft. It didn't matter, they said, that
it was after the election, because the people were voting for elec-
tors, not for the candidates themselves.

"Are you going to be able to vote, Stanley?" Hortense wanted
to know.

"Now, y' know, I don't think I'm going t' make it t' my polling
place. I'm registered in Hastings."

So Ray was the only member of the Bush family qualified to
vote. On Tuesday he went to Gurn Spring and cast his secret
ballot.

In a confidential moment after the others had left the dinner
table that afternoon, Hortense drawled, "I've been most impressed
with your operation of the farm, Ray. You have a splendid farm,
and you're such a capable manager. You should win all the prizes
at the fair, and you deserve to make a great deal of money from
all your delicious products."

Ray blushed. He was pleased by the compliments, but couldn't
think of an appropriate reply. She had said many nice things
before about his work on the farm—things that indicated how
much she admired and respected him. She had a way of fastening
those big brown eyes on his face when he was talking that gave
him a special warm glow, but left him tongue-tied.

He thought back to his unkind prediction last January about
her being a stupid dancer who couldn't cook, sew, or clean. In a
way it had been a correct evaluation.

Hortense hadn't done much in the way of helping with the farm
work and never learned to milk a cow, though she made one
uneasy attempt. The pigs terrified her; the rooster chased her
shrieking from the chicken yard; even the sheep frightened her,
except for the very youngest lambs.

In trying to help Lottie around the house, she was so slow and
cautious that Ray knew his mother could have done the work
faster without her help. Her attempts at sewing were comical—she
couldn't keep her feet moving on the treadle while she held the

material with her hands. Her meticulous table setting, her deliberate salad making, her painstaking sweeping all took more than twice the time they should have taken. "Did I do that right?" she would ask anxiously, wanting so much to help, but not knowing how to do anything.

All of that was understandable, because she was so young—and so unaccustomed to farm life. She had a lot to learn in order to be a good farm wife. But she was so happy here and yearned so to stay. Ray felt sure she could acquire the homemaking skills she needed with experience and his mother's tutelage.

"I do so wish I could stay here the rest of my life," Hortense was saying. "You and Mother Bush have been so wonderful to me—I don't want to go to Georgia. I—I guess I'm a little afraid."

"I wish you could stay here too, Hortense."

His body ached to hold her in his arms and keep her here forever, but Ray couldn't think of any way to prevent it, if her husband was determined to take her south.

On the day after the election, of course, the big news was that Wilson and Marshall had been elected. As far as Harold was concerned, the big news was that he got to ride the trolley car. Since there was no electric railway running through Corinth, he seldom had the thrill of riding the trolley.

"Hi, Uncle Ray," he shouted when Ray met him and his mother at Doe's Corner. "I rode the trolley car!"

When he got to "The Gables" he bellowed it again to his grandmother. Then he yelled, "Look Gramma, I brought my primer, so's I c'n read t' you."

Lottie came out to greet them and hear Harold's chatter about Pa taking them to Saratoga in the wagon and his ride on the trolley. She made a big fuss over him as she always did. He read a few sentences in his book rather haltingly, but at least he was enthusiastic about school now. He didn't mention the little boy who had teased him and called him a cripple. Lottie was glad to see that he had taken her advice to heart and was trying hard to learn to read. He talked about some new friends at school too, so she felt much better about him.

In the middle of the afternoon Lottie went to tend to the butter. She didn't have to churn very often now that they only had one cow in milk. It was time to do it now, though, so she set to work

147

churning in the creamery. The big barrel churn turned round and round with a clacking and swishing noise. The thick stone walls of the creamery bounced the sound back and magnified it. Frequently Lottie had to stop turning the handle and pull out the bung to let the excess air escape. It made a loud explosion like a gun firing in the small building. Lottie knew that Harold was afraid of the noisy churn, so she wasn't surprised that he didn't follow her in the creamery.

While Lottie was busy churning and working the butter, Mary started cooking supper. First she baked a pie with some of the damaged apples that needed to be used before they spoiled. She put on some beets and potatoes to boil and started a huge, thick slice of ham sizzling in the frying pan. When the pie came out smelling divine, she popped some biscuits in the oven. Nothing could beat the combination of odors that wafted from the kitchen.

"Supper's ready! Come and get it," she called, stepping outside the kitchen door.

Hortense and Stanley were just coming back from a visit to some of their friends.

Ray came in from the west orchard, where he had been checking for any apples they might have missed, and picking up the ladders. He washed his hands in the kitchen. Mary looked at him strangely.

"Where's Harold? I thought he was with you," she said in a funny, choked voice.

"I haven't seen him since dinner," Ray answered, looking at her in surprise.

"Mother Bush, is Harold with you?" Mary asked as Lottie came in with some jars of butter.

"Why, no, dear. I haven't seen him since I started churning. He hates the churn and never comes near it. He doesn't like the noise it makes."

Hortense said, "Stanley and I have been gone all afternoon. We haven't seen him at all."

"Oh, my lands sakes!" Mary exclaimed. "Where's he been all afternoon?"

She wiped her hands nervously on her apron.

"Something terrible must have happened to him! It's getting dark outside! He must be lost! Where can he be?"

"Now Mary, he wouldn't get lost on the farm. He knows every

inch of it." Lottie tried to sound reassuring although she was worried too.

Hortense said quickly, "I'll go look upstairs. Maybe he's up there asleep."

Mary started calling, "Harold, come to supper!"

There was no response. Hortense came back and reported that he was not in any of the rooms upstairs. Stanley and Ray went outside and began shouting in all directions.

"I'll go down to the Myers' house and see if he went there," Ray said.

"I'll check th' barn 'n' th' pasture."

Ray strode rapidly down the road, looking in the ditches for an unconscious body—or a dead one—struck by a passing auto.

Stanley went through the barn, yelling Harold's name. Could one of the horses or cows have knocked the little boy down and trampled on him? What a horrible thought. He began to search the pastures for a still form. The animals stared at him curiously. "What have you done t' Harold?" he asked distractedly.

Lottie went to search Jo Henry's shack, since no one was living there now. She did wish Jo hadn't built his pesky tenant house so close to her home. Maybe some gypsies had gone in there for shelter and might have done some brutal injury to the little boy. Lottie didn't trust gypsies; she always locked her doors when they were in the neighborhood.

Mary started out toward the creek. Maybe he had been trying to catch a fish—he dearly loved to fish. He could have fallen in the shallow water and hit his head on a rock and drowned. Her throat closed up as she tried to shout, so what came out was hardly more than a whisper—"Harold!"

The picture of him lying so still upstairs here at the farm two years ago, paralyzed and near to death, tormented her. He had lived that time, but was he dead now?

"Oh, why did I just assume he was with Ray?" she moaned. "Where are you, Harold?" she began to scream, finding her voice at last.

Hortense went to search the cellar. Maybe he had gone down there and been shut in. He was too small to push the heavy doors open—she could hardly lift them herself. Maybe they had fallen on him and crushed him to death.

Everyone was screeching Harold's name. Everyone was frightened and worried. They each had a premonition of some horrible death that might have befallen the dear, innocent little boy.

Ray started back from the Myers' with no news of the boy. They didn't know he was even on the farm. Lottie came back, carrying a lantern. She had searched every corner of the shanty to no avail. Stanley had searched all the pastures and then decided to go look in the Spy orchard on the mountain.

Just as Ray approached the house, he saw a small figure emerge from the barn, rubbing his eyes sleepily.

"Harold!" exclaimed Ray. "Where have you been?"

"In the barn, Uncle Ray," he answered groggily. "I guess I fell asleep."

There was straw clinging to his hair and clothes.

Ray set up a shout that Harold was found, and all the family gathered around. Mary hugged her son and wept tears of relief. Harold couldn't understand what all the furor was about.

"I went in Alban's stall and fell asleep," he said matter-of-factly. "Gramma was churning and the churn scared me, so I tried t' hide from it."

Harold was a much pampered child that night. He was hugged, kissed, and petted. No one thought of chiding him for hiding.

When they went in for supper, nobody minded that the biscuits were burned.

Hortense finally went on her shopping expedition the following week so she would have some warm fall clothes to wear on her trip. At Ida's invitation she spent the night in Glens Falls too. Miserable without her, Stanley caught the early car up to Glens Falls, so he could ride home with her the next morning.

When the family gathered for dinner, Hortense talked animatedly about her shopping trip.

"You can give us a fashion show after dinner," Lottie suggested. "I'm anxious to see everything you bought."

Ray broke into the female chatter with the news that interested him. "I saw the first Canada geese fly over this morning. I've got to. . . ."

"On th' way t' Mexico!" Stanley interrupted. "Isn't that something how they find their way straight. . . ."

"You can always tell when winter's coming," Ray spoke a little louder to drown out Stanley's interruption. "They fly right before

150

the snow every year. Those clouds up there look like snow right now. I've got to get out and plow this afternoon."

"I wish I'd seen them!" Hortense exclaimed.

"Stanley, did you remember to enter my subscription to the *Glens Falls Messenger*?" Lottie wanted to know.

"Yes, Ma, I remembered," Stanley laughed. "You've got to learn t' call it the *Post-Star*, though. It isn't the *Messenger* any more."

"I've called it the *Messenger* as long as I can remember. I'm too old to learn a new name," Lottie laughed at herself, as she took the dishes to the kitchen.

"Show us what you bought, Hortense. Why don't you put on everything and model it for us?"

Hortense took her purchases upstairs and closed the bedroom door. Presently she came mincing down, lifting her skirt daintily, so it wouldn't drag on the stairs. She paraded around with the taffeta underskirt swishing as she walked. The ruffles on a pink lawn blouse peeked out from under the jacket of her dark blue wool suit. The elegant bonnet matched the suit and had a tall, pink ostrich plume to match the blouse. Sleek kid gloves completed the outfit.

"How do you like it, Mother Bush?" she asked, her brown eyes shining.

"I think it's the most beautiful outfit I ever saw."

Stanley cocked his head on one side, put his hand on his hip, and said, "Well now, Tiny, you're just about the prettiest thing that ever came t' Saratoga County. Going t' knock out the eyes of all those people in Atlanta, G—A. Won't be a single southern belle c'n hold a candle t' you. Gotta have your photograph made wearing that outfit."

"I think I found some marvelous bargains," Hortense bragged. "The suit was on sale for $19.50 at Goodson's. The waist is hand embroidered—only$2.95 at the Boston Store. The hat came from there too. They have such bargains, and they gave me S & H green stamps, too. I gave them to Ida—she saves them. I found the boots at Hartman-Mason Company. They're the latest wrinkle with Cuban heels and only $3.50. Do you like them?"

She lifted her skirt and pointed the toe of a neat high button shoe.

"Indeed I do. I like your entire ensemble. I think you're a very smart shopper, my dear. You look splendid, and not at too much expense either."

Stanley offered his arm gallantly and paraded her around the parlor with mock ceremony. He paused in front of the coal stove and bowed ceremoniously.

"Mrs. Bush, may I present Captain Fisher of the *City of St. Louis*. Captain, I'm counting on you t' provide the ultimate in luxury f'r this beautiful young lady. Nothing's too fine f'r my bride. I'll hold you personally responsible f'r her care throughout the voyage. Her whim is your command, Sir."

"You're silly, Stanley," she scolded. She was really becoming quite provoked by his absurd charades.

Lottie agreed with her wholeheartedly. Hortense was suddenly a beautiful and sophisticated woman, and Stanley was an irrepressible clown. Why couldn't he grow up?

Ray observed from the doorway, thinking he had never seen her look so exquisite. If only he could be the one putting his arm around Hortense instead of his witless brother. He felt a twinge of jealousy every time Stanley touched her. She looked pained by Stanley's childish pretense, he was sure.

While Stanley and Hortense went around paying farewell visits to their friends, Ray was busy getting all the farm animals ready to face the long winter ahead.

First he got the Plymouth Rock chickens into the hen house. They clucked their objection to being confined, but he tossed some oats and runty carrots onto the straw floor, and the chickens pounced on them greedily.

Next Ray put the sheep into their winter quarters. They gave him no trouble, following meekly to their shelter on the south side of the barn, but Ray tossed some bunches of clover to them as a reward for coming so quietly and obediently. There was fresh water for them running into the large pig-scalding kettle all the time from the spring on the mountain.

He needed help moving the pigs. Should he ask Stanley or Ma to help him? Stanley always made such a scene about everything he did, and Ray hated working with him. But Ma was an old lady—she shouldn't have to do that kind of work. He hated to ask her when there was a man available. He decided to wait and get Stanley to help him tomorrow.

"Pack your Saratoga trunk, little lady. We're going t' Atlanta, G—A." Stanley made it into a song the next day.

"Here, Stanley, let me fold your shirts. They won't get wrinkled this way."

She began folding slowly and methodically, in contrast to his slapdash method.

"Where are the reservations for the steamship? We must be sure not to pack them in the trunks that we ship to Atlanta."

Stanley pranced around acting foolish. "Well, you see, Captain, we had reservations, but we shipped 'em by rail to Atlanta. Can't you please let us on board, anyway?"

"Why don't you quit acting like an idiot and go help Ray with the pigs? He's waiting for you."

A few minutes later Hortense heard a lot of whooping and yelling outside. Looking out the window she saw a strange procession. She started snickering and soon was holding her stomach, afraid she would pop open her surgery scar from laughing so hard.

"They need a shepherd dog," she said and hurried downstairs.

Stanley was running this way and that, trying to head the pigs in the right direction. He had a big, stout stick that he brandished at first one and then another pig that got out of line. He looked like a cowboy trying to round up wild steers. It was hard to say who hollered loudest, Stanley or the pigs.

Ray was enticing the biggest pig with a pail full of corn, keeping him next to the line fence, and gradually steering him toward the barn. He was trying to keep the parade orderly and calm, knowing that pigs don't like to be herded anywhere.

Stanley couldn't do anything calmly. He had gotten the pigs so excited that they were grunting and snorting and lunging in all directions. Fortunately they were all still young and not very big yet, or they would have trampled Stanley and gone each in his own direction. Finally they all managed to approach the barn, reasonably close together.

Lottie stood by the barn door and closed it quickly as soon as they swarmed through. Ray put a large quantity of corn in the basement of the barn for them, and they began jostling each other grunting with pleasure.

"I enjoyed the circus parade." Hortense told the men gaily, but they didn't appreciate her remark. They couldn't see anything funny about it. Ray held his tongue, but he was furious with Stanley for making such a commotion.

Stoney-faced, he turned away without a word, and Hortense was embarrassed and contrite. Once again her husband had acted the fool, and Ray was justifiably angry. She would have apologized, but Ray stalked off toward the east orchard taking such long strides that she could never have caught up with him.

Lottie had seen the anger in his eyes and the set of his shoulders as he strode off. She knew that a quarrel between these two grown sons of hers could be really serious. It's lucky that Stanley and Hortense are leaving Tuesday, she thought. She certainly didn't want a fight in the family. Ray was normally a kind, generous, tender-hearted man; but around Stanley he changed. Even his own mother couldn't predict what he would do if Stanley provoked him enough. If Ray struck him in anger, he might even kill Stanley, she thought apprehensively.

The last time Ray had been this angry with Stanley, he had shoved him through a bedroom wall. It wasn't his promise to Ma that held him back now, so much as the sure knowledge that Hortense would offer her solicitude to the injured party in a fight. He could imagine her kneeling beside Stanley and kissing and caressing him if he had been hurt. Since he was much taller and heavier than Stanley, it wasn't likely that Ray would be receiving her gentle, loving sympathy. Oh God, how could he bear it? He walked furiously and swung his fists at an imaginary punching bag. "Eve" no longer came to help him through periods of trial. He needed—he wanted Hortense! What had Stanley ever done to deserve her?

On Monday Ray took Stanley and Hortense's trunks and a barrel of apples to Saratoga to be put on the train to Georgia, and then picked up some things he needed in town. He let Alban set a leisurely pace for the long nine miles back on that pleasant Indian Summer day, while he thought back over the time since last June. He had promised Ma to be kind to Hortense, no matter how much he disliked her.

How hard it was to keep his word! How he resented both of them last summer! He kept silent, and in keeping silent, his suppressed anger grew out of all reasonable bounds like an evil cancer. It almost consumed his whole body with hatred and malice.

Then, when Hortense got so sick, he saw her with different eyes. He saw her as a delicate, naive child, as fragile as a butterfly, and as expendable. He was ashamed now of the way he felt before her illness. He should have realized all the time that she was completely guileless and blameless.

How did he feel now that she was about to leave? Would he miss her? No, that wasn't the question. Could he live without her? She had become the only real passion in his life. His love for her had become an obsession that consumed all his thoughts. He felt that the sun wouldn't shine again until she came back to Saratoga next summer. The sweet, dainty, little southern girl had become almost part of him. He would miss those luminous eyes fastened on his face when he talked about his work. He would miss that gentle drawl. Oh, agony —how he would miss her warm, wonderful presence around the house and yard.

What could he do? How could he possibly rescue her from that exasperating, impossible man she was married to? She should not have to put with such a nincompoop for the rest of her life. He was no longer concerned about Stanley being too old for her. After all, Hortense had proved herself to be a mature adult. At thirty-seven Ray didn't feel too old for her either. He racked his brain for a solution.

Hortense was confused also. She needed to talk to someone, but who? Virgie Kinney? No. Virgie couldn't keep a secret—she would tell her mother, and Mame would talk to Mother Bush. Grace? But Grace would tell John, and he might let it slip to Ray. If only Tommy hadn't run away, she could hold him and tell him her troubles. He couldn't advise her, but talking about her problems would at least give her a better perspective.

Since there really wasn't anybody she could trust, she finally sneaked away to the Spy orchard on her last afternoon at the farm. A startled squirrel was her only audience as she began to talk.

"I don't know what to do! Stanley is such an idiot! Isn't there anything else in life for me besides being the wife of a perpetual clown? He is so silly and childish! Did I make a terrible mistake in marrying him?

"Why did I ever fall in love with him anyway? When I was only nineteen, I thought he was a dapper, sophisticated gentleman. I

155

thought he was amusin' and delightful then. He seemed so confident and self-assured, but now he seems so brash. I used to think he was gallant and well-mannered, but now he is just plain rude. Before, he seemed industrious and energetic, but now I think he is wastin' time with a lot of extraneous motions, lookin' busy, but not accomplishin' much."

The squirrel crept out on a limb of the apple tree.

"I was so dreadfully homesick and lonely at Cousin Lilly's house until I met Stanley. I guess I should never have left home, but I was so humiliated when I found out that I failed the teachers examination! And now I can never go home again! With Mother and Papa in Hastin's now, that would be just as humiliatin' to go back there and say that my marriage was a mistake!

"If only I could stay here with Mother Bush and Ray—I love them so much. But every day I hate Stanley more and more. Oh, I am so miserable!"

She waved her arms around in her distress, and the squirrel scampered to hide on the other side of the tree.

"If I try to ignore my problems, I'll probably get more and more resentful. I've tried that. Stanley embarrasses me so when he makes such a fool of himself! What can I do? He never listens to anybody else. He interrupts. He talks, talks, talks, until I think I will go mad! He never has a serious moment—can't carry on an intelligent conversation with anybody!"

She began to sob uncontrollably.

"I was so happy that day at Lake George," she sniffled, "until he told me I would never have a child. Since then I've felt so empty—so unfulfilled. And I'm so scared—scared of goin' on the ship—and scared of goin' to Atlanta. How can we start off in a strange city with only a temporary job for Stanley? He'll probably never be able to hold on to a decent job. I don't want to go."

She felt the hard lumps in her coat pocket—the three pebbles from Mount McGregor. They had become a symbol for her—a reminder of all that was good about her honeymoon. Of the many happy days on her honeymoon, the one day that stood out as completely happy and carefree was the day they climbed the mountain. Then she drew herself up straight.

"There is no point in livin' in fear of what is goin' to happen. God spared my life for some purpose. I made a bargain, and I will have to stick to it. I made a sacred vow to be faithful to Stanley—no matter that now I'm so attracted to Ray. I must try to be a good wife to Stanley and make our life together happy. If that is my only mission in life, then I'll put all my energy into bein' the best wife I can possibly be. I'll put all thoughts of other men out of my mind.

"When Stanley talks too much and interrupts people, I'll try to shush him quietly. I think I'll try touching his arm and whispering for him to stop talking. Maybe I can help him overcome his fault by gentle and tactful persuasion, but I know it won't be easy.

"I really do want to see Kathleen's baby—and Kathleen and Russel, of course. It's not like we didn't know anybody in Atlanta. There's the Lawrences and Cousin Susie Wells too. Maybe things won't be so bad after all."

A mature woman wiped her tears and walked back to the house.

Hortense shivered in the cold morning air early Tuesday as she took one last look around before leaving the farm she loved so.

"Looks a mite different than when we came, doesn't it, Tiny? Getting awful cold."

Stanley talked all the way to Wilton, comparing the icy bleakness of this day with the fresh, green vigor of the day they came last June, pointing out the threshers busy at work on the Varney's farm, and chattering about how wonderful Atlanta would be.

Aunt Lydia had walked over to the trolley stop to see them off.

Wistfully, she said, "This may be the last time I ever see you two young lovers."

When they protested, she shushed them gently.

"I'm an old lady. I don't expect to live forever."

Ray stood back a few steps as they each hugged and kissed the old lady. Then Hortense shed a few tears on Lottie's shoulder as she clung to her in a tender farewell. Ray was thinking miserably that all the joy was going out of his life, when suddenly, wonder of wonders—oh, bliss, oh, ecstasy—Hortense had her arms around his neck; she was kissing him good-bye. Ray put his arms around her and whispered, "I'll miss you," and she whispered, "I'll be back next summer."

With his eyes he tried to tell her that he was working on a plan so they could be together forever. Aloud he said, "Good-bye, Tiny."

The trolley came twanging to a stop. Everyone called out hasty farewells at once, as they climbed aboard.

"Bon Voyage!"

"Good-bye!"

"Write to us!"

"Thank you for everything, Mother Bush!"

"Write us all about Savannah and the ship."

"Good-bye, Aunt Lydia!"

"Come back next summer!"

"Tell Clif's family 'good-bye' for us!"

Aunt Lydia rode back with Ray and Lottie in the buggy.

"Come spend the day with me, Aunt Lydia," Lottie suggested. "You'll keep me from feeling so lonesome without my dear children."

Lottie knew the theshers would be there soon. They were almost through at Varney's and had promised to come to them next. She started early in the day to plan supper, so she would be sure to have enough food ready for that crew of hungry men.

# A VOYAGE AND A PLAN
## Chapter 12

The threshers worked all that afternoon, and were back early Wednesday morning to finish the job. Ray filled the boilers with spring water from the kettle in the barn, while they got the fires started in the coal burners. Soon the hissing and huffing began again out by the barn. It was noisy and exciting. The men threw in bundles of grain to go through the separator. Ray manned the fanning mill, as it winnowed the chaff from the grain, and the golden grain poured out into big bags tied to the mill. Dust and chaff filled the air, stifled their noses and clung to their clothes. Smoke from the steam engine drifted up toward the mountain. It took all day to finish threshing the buckwheat and oats.

The four men were there for both dinner and supper this time. Lottie stayed busy in the kitchen all day, cooking for that ravenous crowd of men.

When they had finished, they counted up 370 bushels in all, so Ray owed them $12.95 at 3½ cents per bushel. He also paid Capen and Howard Richards $2.00 each. Harry Price earned $1.88 for his work, lashing the straw into bundles with the long, sturdy rye stems. In all the threshing cost was $18.83.

Everything had prospered on the farm this year, with the snows, the rains, the sun, and the wind all coming in their proper time and producing an excellent harvest. The barns were overflowing with grain, corn, hay, and straw; the cellar was bulging with vegetables and fruits; and the market crops of livestock, fleece, apples, grapes, hay, eggs, butter, and milk had put money in the bank. Truly the Bushes had much to be thankful for this year.

Two days later a package and a note came from Hortense and Stanley in New York.

159

*Dearest Mother Bush,*

*Here is your birthday present at last! I'm so sorry it is so late, but we just found it in New York. I've wanted to get it for you since the first day I came to 'The Gables.' I hope you enjoy it as much as I did.*

*I can never thank you enough for all your kindness to me while I was there. I'm very lucky to have such a wonderful mother-in-law! Already I miss you so much! I must hurry—the ship leaves in one hour!*

*Give my love to Ray. Stanley says to send his love and belated birthday greetings also.*

> *Much love always,*
> *Hortense*

In the package was a book titled *The House of the Seven Gables* by Nathaniel Hawthorne. Suddenly Hortense's remark when she first toured the house came back to Lottie.

"This house is so big and ramblin'! It's just like *The House of the Seven Gables!*"

Now she understood why Hortense had wanted to give her this particular gift for her birthday. How sweet Hortense had been, lying there in bed, worrying because she didn't have a gift for her. Then she was happy, when the idea of the perfect gift came to her.

Stanley was very lucky to have found such a wonderful wife. Lottie hoped he would hang on to her and make their marriage a success. Now that they were off on their own, there was a much better chance that they would be able to make a satisfactory adjustment. She remembered how hard it was to live with one's in-laws, no matter how congenial.

"What a dear person she is!" Lottie said aloud.

Ray looked up from the *Corinthian* newspaper Clif had sent him and smiled, knowing his mother had no idea how strongly he felt about that.

"Yes, she certainly is." Mentally he was embracing that sweet, wonderful girl again and again.

Lottie and Ray spent Thanksgiving with the Clarkes and the Sprotts at Grant Cottage, where they all gorged themselves until they couldn't hold another bite. The three families always enjoyed getting together at one house to celebrate Thanksgiving and at another for Christmas.

Mr. Clarke suggested that they come again on a warmer day, and he would give them a tour of the Sanatorium.

"That wind would blow you off the mountain today," he laughed.

The next day was even colder, and the winter routine began again. Ray moved the creamer back into the little dining room for the winter. It was too cold to churn in the creamery now.

Lottie moved all her pots, pans, and dishes back to the little kitchen. It would be warm in there all day with the wood cook stove in use three times each day. The struggle to stay warm always began near the first of December.

Ray had plowed every day since the threshing was finished, racing against the elements. When the snow started falling, he hurried out and went to work, plowing the first snow under along with the stubble and compost.

While he plowed, Ray worked on a plan to get Stanley out of the way. He thought he had a good idea this time—one that would really solve the problem of that unfortunate marriage. Working automatically all the time, he mulled over several steps in his plan. Yes, this one is bound to work. He was sure of it.

When the ground froze too hard for the plow, Ray began working on the grapevines. In two days he trimmed 154 young grapevines and laid them down for the winter, covering them with soil to protect them from the freezing and thawing that might injure the vines. Then he gathered up the trimmings and burned all the rubbish in a clearing.

When he brought in the letter from Georgia on Friday afternoon, Lottie ripped it open eagerly.

"I wonder how their voyage was," she said impatiently. Stanley's writing, like his speaking, was in short staccato phrases. "Here's what he says," Lottie announced, as she began to read aloud.

*Tues. 26 PM*

*Dear Ma,*

*Arrived Sunday all O K at Savannah, and will stay two—three days more. Mail will go out shortly so must rush this. Tiny is tired but O K. Have front corner room best in house, large & airy, De Soto Hotel finest in town. Voyage*

161

*from New York rough and stormy. Tiny seasick whole trip.*
*By golly, not romantic like we hoped. Tiny resting in room*
*while I write to you. Didn't eat a thing on whole voyage.*

*Took walking tour of Savannah yesterday. Both love quaint*
*houses and grillwork. Garden walls and fences—very charm-*
*ing. Warm here, many flowers still in bloom. Spanish moss*
*everywhere. Streets have squares where carriages must go*
*around parks—very picturesque.*

*Tiny says be sure to tell you about cute bunch of girls at*
*LaFayette Square. Heard much laughter behind sheets hang-*
*ing there. Girls came out wearing dark blue uniforms—middie*
*blouses, long skirts and light blue ties. Told us were 'Girl*
*Guides.' Played basketball behind sheets so people couldn't*
*see them. Lady named Juliette Gordon Low started their*
*'patrol' last March patterned after English Girl Guides. One*
*showed us how to send semaphore signals. Tiny said wished*
*she could be Girl Guide. Mighty pretty little ladies!*

*Will be off to Atlanta Friday or Saturday.*

*Love from us both,*
*Stanley*

"Well, I'm certainly relieved that they arrived safely. It's a
shame they had bad weather on the voyage. Anyway it seems
that they're enjoying Savannah. I never heard of Girl Guides, did
you, Ray?"

Ray shook his head, imagining Hortense in the garb of a Girl
Guide, looking charming as she always did.

A week or so later when a fat envelope came from Stanley and
Hortense, Lottie was elated to find a souvenir booklet of Atlanta.
She had been curious about what Atlanta was like, and now she
could see for herself. Ray looked over her shoulder as she turned
the pages, exclaiming over each picture. She was amazed at the
many tall buildings. She counted the windows on the Candler
Building.

"Why, it's seventeen stories high! There's the 'Flatiron' Building in the point, and here's the Piedmont Hotel, where Hortense's
cousin Susie Wells lives. Isn't it elegant? The Terminal Station
is a handsome building too."

Ray grunted. He wasn't much impressed by big cities.

"Look, Ray, there's another beautiful hotel—the Kimball House—and here's the Capitol. Isn't this a lovely booklet, Ray?"

"Yes, but these other pictures aren't so pretty, Ma. There's a lot of industry—the steel works, fertilizer works, foundry and machine works. And there's the Federal Prison, too. Atlanta must be very dirty and sooty. And very crowded, too. Look at all the carriages and street cars and automobiles on the streets! I wouldn't want to live there."

He tried to imagine poor, dear Hortense there in the noise and the crowd—closed up in a small apartment with no place to walk outdoors except that busy thoroughfare—with Stanley forever yammering, gabbling, and blathering until she finally went completely crazy.

Ray had his plan ready now. He was sure this one would work. Hortense shouldn't have to live in that noisy, dirty city. She was too nice a girl to be tied for the rest of her life to that infuriating Stanley. Many times she had said how much she loved it on the farm, how she wanted to stay here forever. He remembered her thrilling embrace in the vineyard and at Doe's Corner. It sent him into rapture every time he thought of it.

While Ray worked, he perfected his plan. He confided it only to Alban, who twitched his ears in agreement.

It was just before Christmas, and the spirit of giving was everywhere. Ray didn't see any conflict between his daydreams of annihilating Stanley and the Christmas spirit. After all, what he was plotting was a Christian kindness. He was going to liberate the poor, unfortunate prisoner of an asinine simpleton. He would rescue Hortense from her unhappy marriage, and then she would have a wonderful life on the farm she loved so much. They would adopt several children, and be happy evermore. Ma would teach her to cook all her special dishes, and she would help with the "grandchildren." They would adopt two boys to help with the farm work and a girl or two to help with the housekeeping chores. Hortense had mentioned several times how impressed she was with Ray's management of the farm. He would show her what a good family man he would be too. No matter that they weren't his own—Ray loved all children.

And he loved Hortense with all his heart. What a wonderful girl she was. He thought of the exquisite joy her kiss had brought him that day in the vineyard.

"I think you're wonderful too, and I love you very much," she said, and his heart flipped óver jubilantly. Then the ultimate ecstasy he felt when she kissed him goodbye left no doubt in his mind that she truly loved him, rather than his stupid, vain, obnoxious brother.

There was a Christmas tree for the district school children at the Town Hall on the Friday night before Christmas. All the neighbors were there and enjoyed hearing the children sing Christmas carols. Then they all joined in and sang together on some of their old favorites. Friends greeted each other with love and good will glowing and reflecting on all sides. When the presents were handed out, the children's simple toys were received with joyful exclamations and beaming faces. The only things missing for a traditional Christmas were the snow and the sleighbells.

As he drove the wagon to Corinth on Saturday, Ray eyed the dark clouds. "We might have snow for Christmas yet," he thought, not especially happy about the idea, because it only meant more work for him.

He unloaded the bags of buckwheat flour at Clif's store and ordered the items Lottie had asked him to buy. Harold came bustling in, with his awkward, swinging half-run.

"Merry Christmas, Uncle Ray!" he shouted with his usual vigorous enthusiasm.

"And a very Happy Christmas to you, Harold," Ray responded, giving his nephew an affectionate hug. "I have a present for you."

"You do? What is it?" Harold began hopping clumsily in his excitement.

"Here it is. Open it now, if you like."

Harold ripped off the tissue paper wrapping and found a little book with a picture of a rabbit on the cover.

He sounded out the title carefully, " 'The Tale of Pe-ter Rabbit.' Oh, thank you, Uncle Ray! I'll get Ma to help me read it." Then slowly and thoughtfully he added, "I wonder if it's a white tail."

He was thrilled with the gift and turned several pages looking at the pictures. Then he whispered a secret.

"Ma made something f'r Gramma, and I know what it is."

"Well, that sounds mighty interesting," Ray whispered back.

Clif finished with another customer and then started adding up Ray's order.

He brought out a package that he had hidden behind the counter.

"This is for you and Ma from Mary and me. Merry Christmas!"

"Oh, thanks, Clif. I'll take it home and let Ma open it. And here's something for you." He handed Clif a ten-dollar bill. "Ma thinks you and Mary would rather pick out what you want, than for us to buy something you can't use. She says young people never like what old ladies pick out."

Harold was tugging on Ray's coat.

"Here," he said. "This is f'r you."

He handed Ray a limp, wrinkled piece of paper with a childish water color drawing on it. Ray looked at it carefully. It seemed to be a horse pulling Santa Claus in a wagon loaded with toys and gifts. Scrutinizing it closely, Ray could see a name under the horse. Sure enough, it said, "Delmar."

"Why, that's Delmar!" Ray exclaimed. "I'd know him anywhere. He's pulling Santa with all his toys."

Harold clapped his hands in delight.

"I knew you'd reckanize him, Uncle Ray. Delmar's a good horse. He never kicks the whiffle-tree."

"I'm sure glad about that. When are you coming to see us, Harold?"

"Ma says we might come next weekend. It 'pends on what else Pa has t' do. I hope we can."

When Ray got home with the package from Clif and Mary and the one he found at the Post Office from Stanley and Hortense, he found Lottie in the parlor. She had decorated all around with garlands of evergreens. The fresh, spicy odor of hemlock and pine pervaded the room.

"That looks real nice, Ma."

"Now it really seems like Christmas, doesn't it, dear?"

"Sure does."

He put the packages down on the table.

"Clif and Mary sent this. This one's from Atlanta—from Stanley and Hortense. Do you want to open them now, Ma?"

"Yes, of course. I want to enjoy them now. On Christmas I'll be too busy with the Clarkes, the Sprotts, and Miss Potts here for dinner."

165

They opened and admired their gifts. Immediately Ray began reading his book on the culture of peach trees from Stanley and Hortense. Then he remembered the paper in his pocket. He showed his mother the drawing of the horse and wagon.

"Harold gave me this. He told me that Delmar's a good horse. He never kicks the whiffle-tree."

Lottie laughed. "What a dear boy he is. This will be our Christmas painting." She held it up against the wall. "Get some tacks and put it up here where everyone can see our special painting of Santa Claus."

It would be a white Christmas after all. Several inches of snow covered the ground by Christmas Eve. In preparation for her big dinner party the next day, Lottie made mincemeat and pumpkin pies, apple tarts, a fruit salad congealed in calf's foot jelly, and stuffing to go in the turkey. After Ray brought in the turkey from Saratoga, she plucked and cleaned it ready to go in the oven first thing in the morning.

She looked around the house. Everything was ready. She had put the lovely Christmas bell Mary and Cliff had given them in the center of the table with some of the fragrant hemlock twigs. The beautiful embroidered dresser scarf was on the sideboard. Mary was such a dear to have made that for her! The fall cleaning and regulating had all been done, and the whole house looked spic and span. She had been so busy getting ready for Christmas that she hadn't had time to read her "birthday" book. After Christmas she would settle down to read dear Hortense's gift. She put the souvenir dish from Atlanta on the table beside *The House of the Seven Gables.*

When he got back from Saratoga, Ray started shelling corn in the barn where it was warm, instead of trying to work out in the snow. He turned the crank, and the corn sheller spit out the hard kernels noisily. Ray was feeling good about having money in his pocket, from the $30.07 Clif had paid for the buckwheat flour, and the check for $200 that had come from Schwarz, as his first payment. This had been such a good year that he and Ma were quite well-to-do now.

The festive decorations and the wonderful smells in the house had put him in a real holiday mood. The only thing that would improve Christmas would be to have Hortense here—gay and laughing, blithe and vivacious, as she had been before her illness.

166

In the fall she had seemed somber and serious. It was that stupid Stanley's fault. He had hurt her so terribly with his contemptible attitude. Ray shuddered. That exasperating fool! He would be doing the whole world a service to wipe Stanley off the face of the earth.

Maybe. Just maybe—next year at this time Hortense would be Ray's wife—warm and sensitive, gentle and loving. This might be his last year without a dear, sweet wife to fulfill his dreams. He felt once more the wonderful warmth of Hortense's arms around his neck and the unbelievable sweetness of her lips on his. To have her with him always would be Heaven.

On the day after Christmas Lottie was ill and dragging. I must have the grippe, she thought. It wasn't as much fun to clean house afterward, as it was to make it sparkle before the party.

Yesterday had been such fun. It was truly a merry Christmas with good friends sharing good food and conversation. Lottie showed off her lovely Christmas gifts from Mary and Clif, and from Stanley and Hortense. Practical Ray gave her a new flannel nightgown, and she displayed that with her other gifts. She gave him a new subscription to the *Farm Journal*.

There was nothing elaborate in the group of presents. Mary's hand-embroidered dresser scarf was the most outstanding item. It was not the value of the gifts that mattered, only the love and concern that had prompted the choice of each object.

The eight-pound turkey spent the morning roasting in the oven and sending forth the most delightful and tantalizing aroma. There were enough vegetables and biscuits for twenty people instead of the seven that came for dinner. There was an assortment of Lottie's homemade pickles, and several kinds of desserts were on the sideboard. The big table was so loaded with food that it sagged dangerously.

The Clarkes, the Sprotts, and Miss Potts all exclaimed over the beauty of the feast. Then they did their best to demolish it. Too stuffed to move, they sat and visited all afternoon, reminiscing over past Christmases and good times they had spent together. Everyone inquired about Hortense and Stanley, glad to hear that their trip had ended happily and that they were settled in Atlanta. They all noticed and laughed over Harold's art work of the horse and wagon bearing Santa Claus. They admired Mary's embroidery and all the other gifts.

Mrs. Sprott asked quite innocently whether Lottie thought Hortense and Stanley might start having children any time soon. Lottie hesitated for a long moment before she explained poor Hortense's sterility. Their words of sympathy were echoing in her head now, as she stared gloomily at the mess she had hardly started to clean up twenty-four hours later.

"Oh, how sad!"

"I'm so sorry!"

"The poor dear!"

Sighing dejectedly, she started washing the piles of dirty dishes. As well as being sorry for Hortense, she was feeling sorry for herself. She would have loved a houseful of grandchildren, but Clif and Mary couldn't have any more babies. It seemed that Ray would never marry, so there would be no more grandchildren for her.

By the time Ransom Varney, Jr. stopped in later to collect his money for installing the gutters, she was able to talk to him cheerfully and inquire about his family's Christmas. She also gave him a word of praise, as she did all the hired boys.

"You and Vincent did a fine job on the eaves troughs."

"Thank you, Mrs. Bush. I see Ray banked some dirt up against the house too. You ought to be dry and warm this winter now."

When Ray brought in the mail that afternoon, Lottie's spirits lifted considerably. She tore open the package from Atlanta and found a letter and a grand, good picture of Hortense. She was wearing the outfit she had bought in Glens Falls—the navy suit, the hat with the pink plume, the pink ruffled shirtwaist, and the black kid gloves. It was a lovely pose with a serene expression on her face. Lottie was delighted with this extra Christmas present and wished she could have showed it with the other gifts yesterday.

She noticed how calm Hortense looked. She had to admire her for bearing her burden so stoically, when she was hardly more than a child herself. How fond she had grown of this dear, lovable young woman—and how lucky she was to have her for a daughter-in-law. In her letter Hortense had made a brave attempt to be cheerful, but the frustrations she was going through in Atlanta touched Lottie's heart. She felt sure these were all temporary annoyances that would soon be resolved though. Lottie felt confident now that their marriage would be a happy one.

With deep regret she recalled her indignant feelings when she first learned of Hortense's existence. Why hadn't she trusted Stanley's judgement and his choice of a new bride? With a guilty feeling of chagrin she remembered her ugly thoughts about what Hortense might be like, and her indignation and shock on that first day. At least she could be thankful that she had never put those thoughts into words.

Lottie knew now that she was truly proud of Stanley. Hortense was the best wife he could possibly have chosen to insure a happy and prosperous future. If anyone could possibly make Stanley settle down into a steady, hard-working husband, Hortense could do it. Surely she was a much better wife than he deserved.

On Friday Lottie wrote an eight-page letter to Hortense thanking her and Stanley for the sachet, the souvenir dish, and best of all the lovely photograph. She expressed her hope that all their problems would soon be solved, and told her all about their Christmas celebration and the snow.

*It's too bad you weren't here when we had enough snow to go sleighing. Ray went to Wilton on the heavy sleighs today. He is getting the cutter ready to run tomorrow. You would have loved a ride in the cutter. . .*

She also wrote at some length about how badly she and Ray had felt since Christmas—some sort of influenza or grippe, she supposed.

At last she had time to sit down and read the book that had been her belated birthday present. She was soon caught up in the story of Hepzibah Pyncheon in her rambling old *House of the Seven Gables.*

I wonder if Hortense thought I was like Hepzibah, she mused. I'm certainly old and strange. And with my butter and egg sales, she might think I have a little shop here in my big, rambling house. If I'm Hepzibah, then Hortense is Phoebe. Last summer she came here and brought a breath of sweet sunshine into a dreary old house, just the way Phoebe did.

She smiled at the thought. She was a fast reader and finished the book in two days.

On New Year's Eve Lottie finished the last entry in her diary while Ray was reading the paper. She leaned back in her chair. The lamp flickered. I must remember to put kerosene in it tomorrow, she thought. The chimney needs cleaning too. She had her new diary ready to start tomorrow.

What a long time ago since she had made the entry on the first of January—"Tonight George will have been dead one year." She flipped through the little book one last time. What a lot had happened in that year!

We're so lucky we didn't lose dear, lovable Hortense. She is the very best thing that ever happened to Stanley. Now with her to calm him, Stanley will surely have a long, happy life.

The fatigue brought on by turning through 366 eventful pages in half an hour's time made Lottie decide to go to bed early and not wait to see the New Year in. She hoped that 1913 would provide only tranquil, ordinary memos for her diary.

Behind his newspaper, Ray was thinking through his plan once more. Next summer when Hortense and Stanley come back for a vacation, I'll persuade Stanley to go fishing with me down t' Moreau Lake. We'll go out in the old row boat down there. I'll snag my line and pretend I've hooked a big one and stand up and lose my balance. I'll fall in and yell for Stanley to save me. Then I'll pull him in. I'm so much heavier than he is, it'll be easy for me to duck him and hold him under. It'll look like an accident. I'll say that I tried to save him, but I couldn't. Time after time I'll dive down looking for his body and finally find it, but it will be too late. That'll make me a hero, and Hortense will admire me.

After the shock and sorrow is over—say in a few months—Hortense will marry me. She loves me already; she said so.. Nobody could live much more than a year with that dunce, Stanley. The only reason she has put up with him this long is that she was sick.

Ray examined his plan from all angles, and he knew it would work. They had gone fishing many times as boys. It would be easy to suggest to Ma that they should have fish for dinner, and she would say, "You boys go catch some fish. Hortense and I will cook some French fried potatoes and vegetables to go with it."

By next summer he would be so sure of every move that there would be no possibility of a slip-up. It was his duty to save the lovely lady from her unfortunate marriage. He glanced at Hortense's photograph for the fiftieth time that day and began dreaming again of that heavenly kiss and the bliss of her embrace.

Lottie interrupted his reverie to tell him she was going up to bed.

"All right, Ma. Good-night."

"Good night and Happy New Year."

# EPILOGUE

I closed the little diary. Immediately the spirits sank quietly and submissively back between the covers. The year had been a highly emotional experience for me. I loved Saratoga, just as Hortense had, and was reluctant to leave and come back to my modern world. I sat there captivated and bemused by the strange story.

The little book that was Hortense's parting gift to me was more precious than anything else I could imagine. In it she had answered all my questions in minute detail and revealed a murder plot as well. She had given me her beautiful memories of Saratoga, so now I could treasure them for the rest of my life. I had been on an incredible journey through time and 1,000 miles without leaving my lounge chair!

How wrong I had been when I assumed that Hortense's life was drab and uninteresting! On the contrary, it was full of glamor, passion, and drama. I was shocked by the intrigue she had caused. Could tender-hearted, daydreaming Ray really have been a murderer? His plan sounded so plausible and possible. Could he really have gone through with it? Somehow I couldn't believe it.

A dozen things could have interfered to squelch Ray's plan. Perhaps John Myers or Perle Kinney might have happened along and wanted to go fishing with them. Or somebody might have been using the boat when they got there, forcing them to fish from the bank. Or perhaps a few minutes in that icy water convinced them to become friends and save each other.

Had anyone ever heard the true story of what happened that day? I wondered. Two men had loved Hortense passionately. Which one would have made her happier? Which one loved her or needed her more? How had Fate decided which of the brothers should spend his life with her?

Ray's scheme was really wicked in my opinion, and was not

based on kindness, as he had rationalized. My heart had gone out to him in his loneliness. But surely that didn't give him the right to snuff out the life of another person, even an irritating one. I liked Ray immensely and didn't want to think of him as a murderer.

I could only surmise what had happened on the day Ray decided to put his careful plot into action. I could envisage the two men spluttering and floundering in the frigid waters of Moreau Lake. It was a secluded lake nestled in a forest at the base of the mountain. Nobody would have been near to see or hear the struggle for their human prize. No one could have testified that there had been a murder. Even if there had been a witness, he probably would have considered it an unfortunate accident.

It was easy to imagine Ray's plan working perfectly, and Hortense becoming his bride three months later, just before her twenty-first birthday. Then they might have spent several frustrating years adjusting to each other and trying to adopt a baby, because marriage doesn't guarantee happiness forevermore, as Ray seemed to believe.

But I could also imagine dear, funny Uncle Stanley babbling on and on to the women when they got home dripping wet.

"By golly, that's the coldest water in the whole U. S. of A.! Felt like 't still had ice in 't! Must of been the biggest fish in Saratoga County— pulled Ray in—lost his line 'n everything! Shoulda seen him thrashing about trying t' get back in the boat. So heavy I couldn't get him—pulled me in too. Like trying t' rescue a whale. Nearly drowned the both of us! Lucky I'm a good swimmer—might of had t' dredge the lake f'r us both. Swam a lot in Florida, don't you know!"

# ACKNOWLEDGMENTS

Many thanks to the wonderful people who assisted in the research for this book, especially:

Donald Myers, Retired Superintendent of Schools in Saratoga County.

Harold Bush, who, to my sorrow died before the book was completed.

Violet Dunn, Saratoga County Historian
Beatrice Sweeney, Saratoga Springs City Historian
Sonia Taub, Saratoga Springs Reference Librarian
Joseph King, Curator of Glens Falls Historical Society
Marianne Stolp, Archives Librarian, Metropolitan Life Ins. Co.
Elizabeth Beale, Program Specialist, Girl Scouts of America
Dr. Orra Phelps, Geologist
Suye Gambino, Caretaker of Grant Cottage
Roy Rice, Calligrapher
Franklin Garrett, Atlanta Historian
Bob Ketchersid, WSB Radio Music Detective

| | |
|---|---|
| John Nichols | Ann Dunson Kelly |
| Eric Estes | Richard Evans |
| Helen Myers | Blanche Brown |
| Mary Myers | Leighton Beers |
| Jerome Orton | Joe Hill |
| Clara Swears | Harry Kohlenberger |
| Marion Bush | John Swett |

and especially—Charlie Shepherd

# REFERENCES

DATE BOOK 1912, Charlotte Bush
*The Atlanta Journal*, June 18, 1912
*The Country Doctor*, Arthur Lewis Tubbs, Baker's Plays, 1910
*Country Life*, Vol. 19, 21, 22
*Glens Falls Post Star*, 1912
*Harper's Bazar*, 1912
*Harper's Weekly*, Vol. 55
*House Beautiful*, Vol. 31
*The House of the Seven Gables*, Nathaniel Hawthorne
*Journey to Day Before Yesterday*, E. R. Eastman, Prentice-Hall, Inc.
*Ladies Home Journal*, Vol. 29
*Lake George Guide*, Lew & Fran Cuddeback, 1978 Edition
*Lake George Mirror*, 1912
*Memoirs of the Sanatorium*, G. E. Harker, 1916
Metropolitan Life Ins. Co. Tuberculosis Sanatorium for Employees,
M.L.I.C. 1918
*New York in the Spanish-American War*, U.S. Archives
*New York Times*, 1912
*Outing*, Vol. 58, 59, 60, 61, 1912
*Outlook*, Vol. 96, 97
*Pageant of America*, Gabriel
*Pageant of Saratoga*, Congress Spring Park, 1912
*Public Health Bulletin #44*, Wade H. Frost, Govt. Printing Office, 1911
Acute Anterior Poliomyelitis
*Saratoga—Saga of an Impious Era*, George Waller, Bonanza, 1966
*Saratoga County Heritage*, Ed. Violet Dunn, Salina Press, 1974
*Saratogian*, 1912
*Savannah Morning News*, 1912
*Scientific American*, Vol. 104
*Scientific American Supplement* Vol. 71, 73
*The Theatre*, July 1912